This book should be returned to any branch of the
Lancashire County Library on or before the date shown

Shaw 2/14.		2/14 NFL
18/5/15.		
Fisher 10/15.		
fisher 1/18		
Raw 7/18		
Cole 8/18		

THE DETECTIVE AND THE WOMAN

A Novel of Sherlock Holmes

Amy Thomas

CHIVERS

British Library Cataloguing in Publication Data available

This Large Print edition published by AudioGO Ltd, Bath, 2013.
Published by arrangement with MX Publishing Ltd

U.K. Hardcover   ISBN   978 1 4713 1575 6
U.K. Softcover   ISBN   978 1 4713 1576 3

11833126

Printed and bound in Great Britain by
TJ International Limited

The Beginning

I stared down at the dead face quizzically, wishing I could feel grief. This wish didn't stem from any guilt on my part, but I thought it would make my next few days easier, days in which I would have to project an appropriate face to the world to keep from raising eyebrows and making my escape less certain. Perhaps the word *escape* is slightly dramatic in retrospect, but at the time, it seemed perfectly reasonable. I digress to assert that I had had nothing to do with putting my husband where his corpse now lay, looking as self-important in repose as it had in life. His death was simply a fortunate tragedy. I've always liked paradoxes. Death by heart attack quite often takes the great and good and elderly, but for once it had claimed a man who was young and brutish. Life is so unfair on a regular basis that it seems to save up fairness like a miser saves coins, only to spend it all on grand moments.

I took one last look at my husband's body and turned toward the door, rearranging my expression to one of subdued sadness. I was glad that in the confusion of the night, I had at least remembered to reach into the recesses of my bureau and take out my one black dress, not a colour I usually favoured. I would put it on now, hoping that the costume would make

1

the role come easier. Emerging from the bedroom, I saw that Dr Park was still hanging about the door, his expression one of assumed sympathy. 'I've taken the liberty of arranging everything, Mrs Norton. You have no need to worry about the remains.'

'Thank you, Doctor,' I said in a low tone, taking care to break on the last word. The portly physician patted my shoulder and strode off, looking pleased at his usefulness. I sighed in relief. One obstacle down, but how many more? I walked quickly to my bedchamber, nodding sombrely to any of the staff I passed, my eyes downcast. My own maid, Millie, met me at my room. It was obvious she had been weeping, and for the first time, I felt genuine emotion pierce me.

'It's quite all right,' I said to her, my look appropriately counteracting my words. She helped me off with the rumpled gown that had now encased my frame for over 24 hours and into my mourning dress, an outmoded fashion that enshrouded me and made me feel like a boarding school headmistress. All the better, for the moment. I looked at myself in my glass and saw a face haggard from sleeplessness and worry. No matter that the worry had been caused by the dead man, not the dead man's death—the watching world would see it and pity me.

I dismissed Millie with the command to rest and sat down at my desk. *Dear Barnett*, I wrote,

2

I need you after all.

*   *   *

Sherlock Holmes refilled his pipe for the third time, staring out the window to take in an alley filled with shops so close they seemed to be built atop one another and dotted here and there with south Florida's ubiquitous palm trees. He found it hard to believe that Fort Myers had been a major military outpost during two American wars. Certainly, the army hadn't left it with any particular evidence of regard, and residents had helped themselves to bits of the fort until nothing was left except a vague impression that something large had once stood in the middle of the city. Of course, he thought, seen in another light, the fort's conspicuous absence was evidence of a more peaceful time when trade and expansion predominated instead of entrenchment and strife. But peace was not without its challenges, he was pleased to note. In fact, crime often flourished during such times.

He opened a leather case by his feet and removed Mycroft's letter, unfolding it slowly. Against his own curiosity, he'd done as he was asked, letting his brother's desires keep the letter sealed until he was safely ensconced in the upper floor of the semi-habitable boardinghouse in which he now found himself. Plenty of nights aboard ship he'd been

3

tempted to digest its contents prematurely, but Mycroft's wishes were never idle, and the detective trusted him as much as he trusted himself. He now read its contents by the piercing light of the early-morning Floridian sun.

Sanchez,
I have reason to believe that our mutual friend will soon again be entrusting her assets to me, assets that have been returned to her by her husband's sudden death. You know as well as I do that she is not to be dealt with carelessly; one false move, and we will find ourselves adrift. Miss A sails on the 19th of September. I will alert you to new developments as soon as they are available.

Barnett

No wonder Mycroft had insisted on his waiting until now. He sat back in his chair and smiled to himself. If it hadn't been for the letter's obvious authenticity, he'd have thought it was his brother's idea of a joke. Unbidden, his mind called up pictures of a boy with unusually bright eyes and hat set at a jaunty angle, a boy who had been a girl.

The three years since the Bohemian case had been taken up with the Irishman Moriarty and other problems, and Holmes had filed The Woman's defeat of him away with his other

4

losses, which were few. He thought about them rarely, only letting himself consider his mistakes on occasion so as to avoid repeating them. No human could ever be perfect, he knew, even one with an intellect as near-flawless as his own. And, indeed, his losses were proofs that the world was not entirely devoid of truly clever people. That thought was a comfort in quiet moments.

Holmes's first inclination, a strong one, was to let Miss Adler handle things herself. Whatever Barnett and Sanchez intended for her, however ominous, he had little doubt she could detect and avert on her own, without the interference of a detective whom she probably considered inferior after their last interaction. But Mycroft had sent him, and that was suggestive of a wider plot. The detective's corpulent brother rarely deigned to entangle himself in anything, and he certainly wouldn't waste his time on a matter of insignificance. No, for Mycroft to take such a direct hand in the matter, it had to be something he considered well worth his notice, which warranted at least a cursory investigation.

The tall detective unfolded himself out of the small wooden chair and shed his dressing gown, throwing it over the rough-hewn wooden desk beside the bed. Watson would have hated that, chided him for being untidy, like a gun-bearing nursemaid—Watson, whose evenings would be spent at home now. Mary

5

Morstan would be pleased.

As he dressed himself, Holmes derived grim amusement from imagining Inspector Lestrade's bumbling investigation at Reichenbach. The dogged detective would have seen what he expected to see, as he always did, and then assisted Watson in declaring the younger Holmes dead. For a moment, Holmes regretted being in rural southern America, where he was unable to procure English newspapers, several of which would undoubtedly have run stories about his demise along with Mycroft's amusing attempt at a grief-filled statement. Lestrade would have waxed positively poetic, he was sure. But Watson—Watson, he thought, would been curiously silent. He refused to let his mind dwell there for long. He adjusted his collar and looked at his reflection in the dirty glass affixed to the wall, finding himself convincingly arrayed as an American businessman of the middle class. Makeup and other more complicated arts of disguise could wait. No one should have cause to know his face here, even if Watson's stories had somehow reached them. He closed his mind to speculation like a trap and readied it, once again, to belong to The Case.

Chapter 1: Irene

I stared at myself in the mirror. Pink cheeks, full lips, bright blue eyes. I was myself again. 'You look beautiful, Miss Adler!' said the voice of Doris the theatre attendant, her painted countenance coming into the reflection behind me. *Miss Adler.* The name hit my ears like cold, bitter water, both refreshing and repulsive. I pushed a curl from my forehead and smoothed my satin gown, standing and turning for her to survey me. 'The audience will be dazzled before you start singing!' Doris had a point. The dress was beautiful—flamboyantly violet, trimmed with silver, far from anything the proper Mrs Norton had ever worn. Ten minutes later, I stepped onto the stage and looked out at a theatre full of people gathered to see and hear the spectacle of Irene Adler, Contralto.

It wasn't my first show. That had been in New York City, followed by ten more after the triumph of the first. After that came Boston and then Atlanta, a city still struggling to recover from the devastation of the American Civil War. Those had all been familiar places, places with memories and theatres whose creaky boards I had walked many times in previous years. Now I found myself in Orlando, Florida, a place I had never been before. My American agent, recently acquired through my solicitor, James Barnett, had assured me that the citrus-growers and their secretaries craved entertainment as much as their more established counterparts in the northeast. And so I had agreed to the engagement, looking forward to a change of scenery. I had found it more difficult than expected to put my old life out of my mind, and a singing tour was a welcome distraction.

The crimson curtain opened, and I stepped onto the theatre's dubious wooden platform, hoping the slats wouldn't give way, but I forgot my worries as soon as the music began to play. Singing felt the same way it always had, effortless and at the same time all-consuming, like arms of sound wrapping around me and bearing me away. I willed the audience to fly with me, and as always, I watched them begin to follow, one by one.

Oh Promise me that someday you and I—
tears began to gather in the eyes of the blonde in the first row.

Will take our love together to some sky—
the man in the upper right private box surreptitiously raised his handkerchief to his face.

*Where we can be alone and faith renew—*My eyes found those of a man in the fourth row, simply dressed, not nearly as grand as the society crowd. His face was nondescript, but his eyes were mesmerising, so much so that I looked at no one else for the remainder of the song.

After my last curtain call, I walked backstage to my tiny dressing room, unsurprised to find that the brass lock had been tampered with. The job was professional, likely undetectable by most people, but I was more observant than the average person. I stopped for a moment in the hallway to grasp a solid umbrella as a possible weapon, but I was far from nervous.

I pushed open the door to my dark room, and, sure enough, the nondescript man with the wonderful eyes from the fourth row stood beside my flower-bedecked dressing table. 'Hello, Mr Holmes.' I affected a breezy, nonchalant tone, since any other seemed as though it would heighten the absurdity of the situation even further.

Mr Holmes smiled a nearly imperceptible smile and bowed slightly. 'Miss Adler, it is a privilege to make your acquaintance once again. I'm glad your senses have retained their previous acuity.' What a thing to say to a lady—and yet, it felt like a high compliment.

'I'm afraid I can't say the same for you, Mr Holmes, leaving evidence of a break-in like that.' I was teasing him, and he knew it. The almost-imperceptible scratches on my door were as intentional as a calling card left on a silver salver. He smiled sardonically and pressed his fingertips together.

Just then, I heard a knock on the door, and Doris popped her head in, her eyes nearly bulging with surprised when she saw Mr Holmes. 'Doris, this is my friend, Mr Smith,' I said quickly, not sure he'd want his name known.

'I just wondered if you wanted some coffee, Miss Adler,' said the girl, while her face said *I'll get out if you say so.*

I smiled. 'I'd love some, and please bring a cup for Mr Smith, too. Oh, and make sure no one else comes in.' She nodded and scampered off, relieved.

'I must say, you've settled back in nicely,' said my companion, looking around the room and then at me. His words held a slight edge, as if the unspoken corollary was that he'd expected something else and been disappointed.

'I did what I'm best at,' I answered, my chin slightly aloft. 'I escaped.'

'Did you?' I didn't like the way he said it, as if he knew all my secrets. In fact, a chill started to spread through my centre and into my throat. Sherlock Holmes didn't do things for no reason.

'Why are you here?'

'It's your—escape, as you express it. I have reason to believe all is not as it seems.'

'I can easily believe that something is afoot if Sherlock Holmes is in my dressing room in Florida,' I answered tersely, annoyed at my own anxiety. 'I didn't suppose you'd come to admire my singing.'

'On the contrary,' he said, easing onto one end of the garishly pink sofa opposite my dressing table, 'your singing was magnificent.'

I couldn't help feeling slightly gratified, but I masked it by looking out into the hall for Doris, who came a moment later with a tarnished tray holding two mugs of the theatre's tepid coffee. I noticed no one lurking about outside, so I assumed she'd done a capable job of chasing off any admirers or stray crew. I slipped her a coin as she handed me the tray, and she blushed and grinned. 'Thanks, Miss A.' She traipsed off like the teenager she was, whatever age her face tried to claim.

I came back into the room to find that Mr Holmes had wiped his face clean of makeup, unmasking the sharp, refined features that were burned into my memory. He had fooled me once, but he would never do so again, I believed.

I turned the chair from my vanity table to face him and held out one of the chipped mugs. He took it, his long, tapered fingers closing around the handle. I wondered suddenly if he'd brought his violin to America, the one Dr Watson mentioned so often in his stories.

'Now, Miss Adler, I need to know what brought you here, your story. I hold out hope

11

that it will give meaning to mine.' The tall detective sipped the coffee, grimacing slightly at its taste, but continuing without comment. His statement seemed oddly metaphysical, but I knew he meant it literally.

'Why should I trust you?' I asked, knowing that I would, but wanting him to persuade me all the same.

'I'd say the level at which we can trust one another is fairly even,' he said drily, leaning back into the sofa and half-closing his eyes. I laughed. It was certainly true. Our last interaction had included mutual deceit, disguise, and blackmail. Strangely, however, it seemed to me that we knew each other very well.

I pushed my feet into the floor and clasped my hands together. I had told my story to no one except Barnett, and even he knew very few details. But Mr Holmes was different; telling him would be like telling a doctor or maybe a phonograph record. Not easy, but not personal, either.

'When I left London, Mr Holmes—'

'Holmes,' came a deep, calm voice from somewhere inside his languid form. 'Dispense with the Mister.'

'I'll be Irene, then,' I answered quickly, not wanting to surrender an inch in our long game, whatever it was we were playing.

'Mr—I mean Holmes, after Godfrey and I left London, we went immediately to Belgium

12

for our honeymoon. You will have received my note the day we left, I believe.' He nodded his head with his eyes closed, looking for all the world as if he was paying no attention whatsoever. But I knew better.

'Godfrey's character remained steady during the trip. He had never been talkative about his past, but neither had I, so I didn't hold it against him. He had always seemed a kind, openhearted man, and no one had an ill word to say about him, except that he was overly popular, but I saw that for myself and never detected anything amiss in his manner. I was very happy during my honeymoon, happy and still, I admit, proud of my little defeat of the greatest detective in London.' I looked up, but Holmes's face did not register any change at this.

'Few, if any, know the truth about Godfrey's family. He was distantly related to an earl, and it had never seemed a significant connection until one month before the wedding, when Godfrey informed me that he had learned that he was the heir to a large estate in Yorkshire. My fortune, gained through my career, was enough to support the manor, which was rich in land but deficient in money. Our friends assumed Godfrey and I meant to move to America, but our intention from that point on was to take possession of the family home. I did not mind the idea of secluded country life. After spending my years from fourteen to twenty-seven touring the world, I felt ready to settle down with a good man—a much better one, I thought, than others I had known.'

I stopped to take a drink of my now-cold coffee, and Holmes stood up and turned to the shelf behind the sofa, which was empty except for a tattered grey afghan that was redolent of mothballs. He handed it to me. I hadn't realised I was chilled, but even in Florida, an old theatre can be draughty. 'Your hands turned pale,' he said, by way of explanation. I thanked him and tucked the afghan around myself, glad for a reprieve before the most difficult part of my recollection, the years I would have liked to forget.

'The trouble started when we reached West Yorkshire. I can't—I still can't explain how quickly it happened. I flattered myself before that I was not a stupid woman, Holmes, but I had been completely taken in. Godfrey was nothing like the man I had known. It immediately became apparent that he had married me for my fortune, the one thing he did not possess to go along with his property and the lifestyle of the landed gentry he sought. He told me very quickly that he had known about his inheritance far longer than he had let on—since before our first meeting, in fact.

'I was shaken, but I planned my escape, determined not to be beaten so easily. He was too vigilant. The man who had been able to deceive me was able to retain power over me by having servants in my way constantly, people who believed he was the kindest of husbands to be so solicitous of his wife's needs. Outwardly, I lived the life of a princess. Inwardly, I felt as if I would die. I could go nowhere alone, do nothing without being watched. My only recourse would have been to injure or kill one of the staff and go alone into the Yorkshire countryside. In London, I would have risked it with a sedative in the teacup of a maid, but in Yorkshire I had access to nothing and no knowledge of the area. I was trapped.'

As I finished my statement, I saw Holmes's hand clasp into a fist inadvertently, the first sign of acknowledgement he had given in many minutes. I surmised that his quick brain was producing in him the feelings of a trapped mind, my captive feelings.

'I will not explain all the details of my relationship with my husband. It is hardly necessary and excessively painful to recall. Suffice to say that he did everything to me that a man can do to make a woman's life miserable, both mentally and physically. I had been with unpleasant men before, but his triumph made him crueler than anyone I had ever known. The only hold I had over him was music. During our courtship, I would sing to him almost every night, and he had professed great fondness for my voice. That, at least, was not a lie. When we were married, he would beg

15

me to sing for him, over and over, and I would refuse. It drove him mad, but I never cared what he did then because I knew that I had kept something for myself. It kept me alive, that one thing.'

I leaned forward. 'One day, Holmes, it happened. We were eating dinner in the evening, and Godfrey complained of stomach discomfort and went to bed. I was relieved because he did not insist that I accompany him. I ate a relatively pleasant dinner under the eyes of the servants and went to my room to allow my maid to undress me for the night. Before she could do so, Godfrey's valet came rushing to the door to alert me that my husband was in unendurable pain and needed the doctor, who was immediately sent for. I went to Godfrey's room and found him sweating profusely and swearing while clutching his chest. I was in a daze. It hardly seemed possible that a figure who held such terrible power in my mind could be lying powerless against some invisible malady. Wild thoughts of murder rushed through my brain, thoughts of the ease of doing away with him in such a weakened condition, but I stood and stared at him as they came and then passed like cooling firebrands. The doctor arrived from the village an hour later and pronounced Godfrey's condition serious. He gave him something for the pain, but that was all he was able to do. My husband died later that night, at about midnight. His death was attributed to heart failure, and the inquest was conducted quickly and seamlessly.

'I was free, Holmes, and the law guaranteed me the return of my money. In the three years we were married, Godfrey had been so concerned about house and grounds that he had been scrupulously careful with my fortune. Had he wished, he could have taken action, I know, to connect the money to the estate more firmly, but he was so convinced of his own ability to manage every detail that he had not yet done so.

'I was tempted to fly immediately, as I think you can imagine, but I maintained an appearance of genteel mourning until all the legal steps were completed. Once my solicitor, James Barnett, assured me that my money was again my own, I arranged to travel to America. Music has been the one friend who never betrayed me, so I took it up again. Singing was my livelihood in the past, but I saw no reason why I could not return to it for different reasons. I planned my life very differently, Holmes, but this is what I have left, a voice and a fortune.' I could not help the slightly bitter note that crept into my voice near the end, but I supposed he expected it. He had helped too many unfortunate women to be unaware of the usual results.

'There you have it, Holmes,' I finished, sitting back in my uncomfortable chair and looking at him full-on, my eyes challenging him to betray his inner thoughts. He gradually roused from his apparent torpor and sat up straight, his eyes meeting mine without judgement or comment.

'Thank you, Irene,' he finally intoned, sounding slightly awkward over my name. 'I had surmised the greater part of your circumstances correctly, but your narrative has supplied key details of which I was otherwise unaware.' He stared at me for a moment, his eyes curiously bright. 'It is not my usual practice to disclose my methods to anyone except Dr Watson during a case, but I am confident that in you I have a listener who will be able to ascertain and comprehend what I say. In short, Irene, I hope that by the end of my tale, we will be allies.' His eyes presented a challenge as open as mine had been.

'That is a somewhat extraordinary hope, Holmes,' I shot back, 'considering our previous interactions.'

'Not at all,' he returned, with the ghost of a twinkle in his eye. 'It is merely a logical assumption.' I smiled at him, unable to stop myself, remembering the night I had dared to greet him in the street while dressed like a boy—an unnecessary greeting for an extraordinary man, a man who had been entirely impossible to ignore. Three years had changed me a great deal but seemed to have changed him not at all.

Chapter 2: Holmes

Irene Adler was an unusual woman. That was hardly necessary to consider. Holmes had been aware of it since the moment he'd recognised her as the successful mastermind of his defeat in the Bohemian affair, and now, as he saw her before him, the impression was strong once again. Nevertheless, he knew, the human heart was consistent—consistently susceptible, even in a genius. Men and women, both the stupid and the clever, had been taken in by the opposite sex since the dawn of time, he didn't doubt, and would be taken in until it ended. Like many others, Irene had seen what she desired to see and ignored the rest. She had been foolish—understandably so, perhaps, but she had also been strong. A weaker person would have succumbed to despair long before three years had passed, and he could hardly fault her for being deceived by another when he had been deceived by her. He could not, however, keep himself from wishing that her suspicions had served her better. Weakness was more painful than usual when he saw it in one to whom he had attributed unusual intelligence. But, as he knew too well, no mind was infallible.

The detective leaned forward and rested his arms on his knees, looking into The

Woman's delicate face. He wished, as he had throughout the evening, that he had his pipe. The oversight had been deliberate, however, as it had no place in his chosen disguise, and he satiated himself by thinking of it lying snugly in its leather pouch in his hotel.

'The story starts,' he began, 'with my death.' He relished the quick look of surprise that flashed across her features. He always had enjoyed a shocking beginning. 'After your departure, my life proceeded largely as it always had, except that I began to detect a hidden pattern that I had never before seen, as if the underworld of London were running according to a shared agenda. There was a regularity to it, a deadly efficiency that nothing so vast can reach without someone or something orchestrating its movements. I will not tax you by explaining all of my processes, but I discovered the unmoved mover, as they say, to be a man named James Moriarty, an Irish professor of unassuming appearance and remarkable mind. He set out to kill me, and it became evident fairly quickly that I would not be safe while the man remained at large, free to use his vast organisation as he willed. Watson went with me to Switzerland, and I met Moriarty at Reichenbach Falls, arranging things so that my friend would find evidence of a scene that appeared to be the death-place of both Moriarty and myself. The first assumption was correct; Moriarty met his death by equal parts my hand and the inexorability of the Falls. I escaped, however, and traveled immediately to Florence, Italy, from whence I contacted my brother. My object was to remain absent from England, or, indeed, from the knowledge of the public, until enough of Moriarty's associates had been apprehended that I might return without unreasonable risk to Watson or to the investigation. Such is still my intent.

'Now to the part of the story that concerns you. During my time in Florence, my brother, who works for the British government in a diplomatic role, sent me a letter, a request that I sail to America, and a note insisting that I not open the enclosed missive until I arrived. More than that, he asked that I wait until I had reached a town south of here called Fort Myers, an outpost during the American Seminole and Civil Wars. I didn't know what he meant by the request, but my brother's mind is very like my own, so I did as he asked. Truthfully, without a firm objective, I grow irritable, and I was glad of having a purpose.'

Holmes's deliberate omission of the scope of Mycroft's influence was, he considered, entirely necessary. What he had said was technically true and hopefully sufficient to satisfy Irene's immediate curiosity. He trusted her mind enough to believe that she would not betray him in a naive manner, but he did not trust her nearly enough to be willing to share internationally sensitive information in a wanton way. Whatever else was true, Mycroft must be protected. The Holmes brothers did not have a code; they simply shared keen enough intellects to understand the delicacy of one another's positions in the world. Mycroft could certainly take care of himself, but Holmes did not intend to complicate his task by bringing The Woman into more than necessary confidence.

He noted with pleasure that Irene was completely engrossed in his tale, her slim body alert as she followed his every word, her tiny hands pressed against the arms of her chair. 'When I reached Fort Myers, I opened this.' He handed the paper to her. No need to be irritatingly coy. Her eyes scanned the note once and then again, and her face gradually lost colour and gained it again in a heightened fashion. Holmes watched her expression shift from polite interest to malignant anger in seconds, a remarkable transformation. At once, her demeanor changed to one of focused purpose as her anger was instantly sublimated, a process Holmes recognised and respected.

'Continue,' she said very quickly, a slightly breathless note in her voice, but she sat back in her chair, the only evidence of her agitation the vice-like grip with which she still clasped Barnett's letter in her right hand.

'You will have already connected this letter with your recent circumstances, but I had no such references, though I immediately surmised what my brother already understood, that this letter concerned yourself and those who wish to harm you in some way. I believe my brother's insistence that I wait to read it related to the fact that he thought I might be reluctant to help one who had so effectively defeated me in the past.' Holmes smiled to himself. 'Unlike my brother, however, I do not hold grudges. In fact, since we have been fortunate enough to meet again—(the word *fortunate* came off his tongue with a razor-edge)—I am happy to say that I bear you no ill-will. On the contrary, I find your wit refreshing.'

Irene's face remained blank, and Holmes couldn't tell if his admission had had any effect on her. It wasn't a lie, but his inclusion of it at that particular moment wasn't entirely artless, either. He intended to have Irene Adler for an ally before the evening was over, and he was determined to play his cards until the right one hit the table.

'I will help you.' Holmes tried in vain to keep his surprise at Irene's words from registering on his face. 'You've no need to keep courting me, Holmes.' Her eyes burned into him like the coldest ice. 'I know that once you've taken a case, you won't rest until it's solved. If I or my property is in danger, I can be in no better hands than yours. That is not a compliment; it is a statement of fact.

Do not expect my trust beyond this, but I will help you.' She ceased speaking, and Holmes nodded once. She returned the gesture. 'Now, tell me what you've learned.'

'I knew that Mycroft would not have sent me to south Florida without a definite purpose, and I soon discovered what it was. A man called Alberto Sanchez, a native of Central America, owns a profitable citrus grove ten miles outside of the city of Fort Myers. He is not yet wealthy, but will be once his harvest is concluded. The area is largely peopled by field workers and fruit magnates; he is one of the latter category, of course, a very recent newcomer. In the three weeks I have resided in town, I have received the impression that he is on the edge of polite society—hardly the darling of the most respectable, but with money that makes him more than a pariah. Society I find more interesting than expected, frankly.' Holmes put his hands together and pressed his fingertips to one another, relishing what he was about to say.

'The belle of Fort Myers, Irene, is none other than Mrs Mina Edison, the young and lovely wife of the brilliant inventor Thomas Edison.' To Holmes's satisfaction, Irene's smile hid neither her surprise nor her pleasure at learning this.

'But why are they in Florida, Holmes, without all the conveniences of the North?'

For the moment, she appeared to have forgotten her own troubles in her sudden interest. Holmes noted that she looked more alive, more like the woman he'd encountered three years earlier, than she had all evening.

'The family divides its time between New Jersey and Florida, spending the cooler months in the South and the warmer in the North, a practice that is not unpopular among Americans with enough disposable income to make it feasible.'

'What else have you learned?'

'I will happily tell you, but the story will better accompany our train journey in the morning. If we catch the 7:30, we'll be in Fort Myers by late afternoon.'

'You wish me to come with you, then?'

Holmes looked at Irene in dead earnest. 'Of course. I came with no other object. Your presence is required to carry the case to a successful conclusion.'

'Well, Holmes, when you put the offer in such romantic terms—' Irene looked up from contemplating the faded green carpet and half smiled 'I take it you've figured out a way to explain to the theatre why their prima donna is about to be in absentia for the remainder of her scheduled dates.'

'Naturally. On the very morning of the disappearance of Irene Adler, Annie Hart will arrive requesting the theatre for her personal use. The management will be delighted to have the Bowery Girl herself, and the absence of the charming but as-of-yet lesser-known Irene Adler will be a convenience rather than a hardship. Thankfully, Miss Hart owes me a favour. I confess that getting rid of your manager presented a greater challenge, but in the morning, he will find himself in receipt of a telegram supposedly composed by yourself, declaring that your nerves have been frayed by your hectic touring schedule and declaring your intention to rest in seclusion. A hefty sum of money will be wired to him as well, a supposed gift from his appreciative, though delicate, client. He will be instructed to await your communication at a future date.'

'You arranged all this beforehand?'

'Of course, I could not afford to lose time after contacting you.'

'You were that sure.' It wasn't a question. Irene stared at him with what appeared to be a mixture of admiration and something that went deeper than annoyance but stopped short of loathing, something like resistance.

'I hoped,' Holmes answered truthfully. He held out a train ticket, and she took it without hesitation. 'In the morning, gather your funds and belongings and come to the station. If you see me, do not acknowledge it by look or word, and I will do the same. I am not known here, but I don't want to take chances this close to the scene of events, especially in a place where a stray concertgoer might recognise the divine

Miss Adler. Go to the third carriage. I have arranged for it to remain empty.

'Once on the train, your name will be Mrs Lavinia James, wife to Bernard James, a British investor with more money than sense, who is travelling in the new world to enjoy himself and discover whether or not citrus fruit is the key to augmenting his fortune. The emphasis is on the enjoying; Mr James finds it necessary to attend as many social functions as he can and make himself as charming as possible to everyone. He is eager to introduce his American wife, who has been nursing her sick sister but is now joining him.'

'Your wife,' said Irene drily.

'Well, you could hardly play the role of my valet,' said Holmes, smiling to himself, 'unless, of course, you still possess that charming outfit you donned during our previous encounter.' The Woman did not reply.

*   *   *

Irene's hotel was in a much more fashionable part of the city than the detective's. He deposited her at the door and took off down the dark street, musing. He hadn't minded his time alone on the Continent and then in this strange climate where autumn brought nothing more than the slightest addition of a breeze to make the sun less unbearable. He liked the focus that solitude brought, the quiet clarity.

And yet, solitude had also been the siren that whispered the craving into his mind and placed the syringe in his hand. Past solitude had made him dependent. Truthfully, he needed the friction of other minds, the whetstone of communication, to keep him from sliding into the grey. When he thought about it, he missed the comfortable ease of Watson, the familiar, practical turns of mind, the errors and the occasional triumphs. He missed the rhythm. He even missed the irritation, the annoyance that reminded him he was more than a machine.

Irene was different. If Watson was a pipe and slippers before a warm fire, she was a Nor'easter, an American storm that blew wherever it chose and sent everything in its path head-over-heels. With surprise, Holmes realised that he felt deep anger, rage against a dead man. No person had the right to lock up something so wild.

Chapter 3: Irene

Two flights of stairs took me to the hallway that contained my room, a generously-sized suite with obscenely opulent wooden furnishings obviously designed to appeal to Florida's new money. The hotels in New York and Boston had installed lifts to save guests from the stairs, but Orlando was a younger sibling playing catch-up in many ways. I didn't mind. I enjoyed the exercise after my mind-whirling evening. Once inside, I lay down for a moment on the hideous yellow coverlet to collect my thoughts.

Hours before, my life had stretched before me in a predictable manner, as predictable as the life of a travelling performer can be. I had not let myself think beyond the singing, the dates that would follow dates for as long as I could continue. I would grow richer, and my memories would grow further away in time, at least, if not in feeling. I would be the world's Irene Adler again, and my mind would be forced to acquiesce, to find its own occupation in between the different places that would all come to seem the same in the end.

Holmes's arrival was like a splash of saltwater to the face, the sting and then the awakening. Perhaps Barnett's dastardly plans for me, whatever they might be, were blessings in disguise, for they had acted as the catalysts to draw salvation near. I laughed at the drama of my own thoughts. What sort of salvation was six feet of arrogance and the promise of endless swordplay? And yet, I experienced relief from a feeling I hadn't known I still had, the desperation of a mind shuttered and set aside. What Holmes offered me was a chance to think freely, and that felt as close to salvation as anything I could imagine

I allowed myself the luxury of a few moments of contemplation and then roused with purpose. I quickly collected my small belongings from around the room and placed them in my carpet reticule. My clothes went into the sturdy trunk that had served me well through the crossing and all my travels. I felt like a criminal packing my gowns; my manager always arranged for someone to pack them for me at the end of each city's run, and I was far from skilled at doing so myself. I hoped that whatever plans Holmes had for us upon our arrival in the southern city would include enough time for my dresses to recover before being worn. Part of me missed the quick hands of my Yorkshire lady's maid, but I did not miss her constantly watchful eye or loose tongue. My manager, Slade, had begged me to take on a maid or companion of some sort to travel with us and provide company for his secretary, but the haunting memories of my married life had made me desire the freedom to be alone and do as I wished. I usually did very well on my own. In fact, I had begun to think I might never engage another permanent maid. Slade was more than enough, with all of his fussing about my supposed comfort and fawning over my talent. I was grateful for his abilities, which had smoothed my way considerably, but I knew that I would not miss him.

After I had finished packing my possessions, with widely varying degrees of efficiency, I considered the metal safe tucked in the back of the closet. It contained my personal funds and the one piece of fine jewellery I carried with me, a diamond necklace I had inherited from my mother when I was a child in New Jersey. I had a sizeable portion of money in my personal possession at all times, a practice Slade deplored as being unsafe. This, too, was most likely a result of the confines of my marriage, but even before my nuptials, I had been wary. I did not like to be at the mercy of others any more than was absolutely necessary. Slade had no idea how adept I could be at defending myself, should the need arise. I decided to leave the safe opening for the morning, and I decided not to tell Holmes about the money. Wiser to keep something to myself in case of emergencies. He had tried to beat me once and only lost on a knife's-point. I could not afford to trust my wits alone to save me again.

Before I slept, I set the alarm clock for 6:30. The theatre would not expect me until at least 3:00 in the afternoon, and my only other engagement was lunch with Slade and an enthusiastic music lover at 12:30. If all went to plan, I would be far gone and my manager paid off before anyone recognised my absence. Sleep was long in coming, but I didn't mind. Excitement hadn't kept me awake for quite some time.

*　　*　　*

Ding I was fighting a black dress that wouldn't stop wrapping its silky, choking arms around me. *Ding* The corpse on the table kept talking to me, endlessly, about where to place my assets, but it was the corpse of the king of Bohemia with the voice of Sherlock Holmes. *Ding* I fought to the surface, emerging into the smell of stale cigars and the feel of silken bedsheets. I arose quickly, washing my face in the porcelain basin and dressing myself in a plain brown shirtwaist and long tan skirt. I rang for the porter, a near-child, as soon as I was decent and requested a light breakfast, which I ate as quickly as possible. I rang for him once again, and when he arrived I instructed him to take my trunk to the lobby. 'Are you going away, Miss Adler?' he asked curiously, fingering his forelock. The hotel staff had been told I was some sort of musical celebrity, and they were aware that I had been engaged for a run at the theatre, a run in these parts usually being construed as anything more than one night. 'I need my things at the theatre tonight,' I answered with a ready smile. 'Someone from there will come by to pick it up.' This satisfied the boy, and he took it willingly after being handed a few coins. I was glad that Holmes had entrusted me with a few unmentioned details. At least he trusted my judgement that much.

My last act before leaving the room for the final time was to open the safe. I had an irrational, uncomfortable feeling that the contents might have disappeared during the night, but there they were, as snug as ever. I secreted the roll of American money in a pouch I carried close to my body underneath my clothing. The necklace I put on, taking care to hide it completely under the high collar of my practical shirtwaist. I picked up my reticule and proceeded downstairs, stopping in the lobby to enquire after a cab 'for the theatre.' The white-haired steward behind the small desk smiled uncomfortably widely and replied in the hushed tones of a doctor addressing an elderly hysteric. News of my 'fame' and generous pocketbook must have reached all quarters, I reasoned. He promised me a coach as soon as one could be procured, and I settled in to wait, noting from my watch that I still had half an hour to make the train station, which was only about ten minutes' ride away. I sat down in a faded brocade chair and studied the place, a mixture of American innovation and tasteless nods to old-world finery, emphasising the worst of each, from the wallpaper (peeling at the very edges) that depicted what looked like palm trees covered with grotesque monkeys, to the fat, unpleasant cherub statues that stood on either side of the oversized staircase.

Thankfully, I was not left to wait in this

paradise for long, as a cab arrived within five minutes, driven by an elderly, hunched man, who was too abashed by my presence to make eye contact. The steward simpered proudly at having procured my transportation so quickly, and I thanked him monetarily, taking advantage of the air of good will to enquire after my trunk. 'I sent it down for my theatre to collect,' I said in my most innocent, whimsical voice, 'but I think I'd like to take it with me now.' The steward was only too happy to oblige me by yelling for two adolescent porters and having them hoist it onto the coach with the help of the aged driver, who seemed to take it all as a matter of course.

'The theatre, Miss?' he asked before we set off, his voice thin and reedy.

'No, the train station, if you please,' I said, sounding unconcerned.

'Very well,' he answered, in a tone that seemed to say *none of my business anyway.* I wasn't overly concerned; if he chose to tell the story later, I would be long gone. Nevertheless, I tipped him double the usual amount when we arrived at the platform, and he arranged for my trunk to be stowed. We had arrived with ten minutes to spare, so I purchased a cup of terrible coffee from a slatternly woman who had a vague excuse for a stall in the middle of the warehouse-like wooden building that served as a station. I considered buying two, but I supposed that would arouse the sort of speculation Holmes was trying to avoid. Thankfully, no one appeared to recognise me, and I did not even clap eyes on my travelling companion. I boarded the train considerably more relaxed than I had begun the day, proud of myself for successfully navigating the morning's small pitfalls.

I made immediately for the third car, taking care not to walk too quickly. The train was surprisingly luxurious. I had expected something more provincial, but it had all the accoutrements of the trains that had carried me through New England, the leather and velvet and smartly-uniformed staff with every desire to please. I chided myself for my prejudice. The newness of Florida's prominence did not necessitate a complete lack of taste, hideous hotel vestibules notwithstanding.

I entered the third car eagerly, far more enthusiastic about seeing Holmes than I had expected to be. But there was a problem. The car was occupied, but not by Holmes. Instead, my elderly cabdriver sat placidly hunched over an almanac, sipping coffee from the same stall I had visited. He looked up as I entered, his cloudy eyes barely visible through matted grey locks. My mind raced. Uppermost was annoyance at Holmes. Where on earth was the man, and why hadn't he upheld his promise of an empty car? Furthermore, how could I get rid of the intruder? Just at that moment, the aged driver straightened up, said 'Good morning, Mrs James,' and began to take off his face.

Annoyance instantly followed recognition. 'Whatever do you mean by this, Holmes?' I hissed, keeping my voice low. I had no idea how far sound would carry on a train (though Holmes probably did, hateful man), but I didn't want to risk alerting curious listening ears.

'Call me Bernard from now on,' he replied in a low voice of his own, before continuing in a more normal tone. 'I couldn't risk anything going wrong, so I included myself. That is all.'

'Entirely all?' I asked suspiciously, taking my seat on the bench opposite him.

'Well,' he admitted, 'after you spotted me so quickly yesterday, I thought I might challenge myself and see if my subtler abilities had lost their sharpness against the recognition of one who knows me. I see they have not.'

I wanted to be angry, but I could see that he meant the statement literally and as no kind of comment on my observational abilities. 'It was the eyes,' I said quickly. 'Yesterday, they were your own. Today, their cloudiness belonged to someone else.'

'Well spotted,' said Holmes, pulling forth a small pipe. 'I did not mind driving a cab with the eyes of another, but only the eyes of the great detective himself could be put to the purpose of meeting Irene Adler again.'

36

I wondered if he intended to mock me, but he seemed dead serious. He puffed away at his tobacco for a moment and then drilled me with his gaze. 'From now on, we are Bernard and Lavinia James. Use those names as often as possible until they are second-nature. We can't afford to slip.' I nodded, slightly annoyed at his schoomasterish tone. I certainly wasn't stupid enough to have failed to assimilate the necessity of subterfuge.

'Come, my dear Lavinia, and let me show you the letter I've received from our friends.' Holmes motioned to me to join him on his side of the car, and I did so, unable to keep from smiling at the conspiratorial glint in his eyes.

'Very well, Bernard,' I answered, sitting myself down primly. Holmes handed me a sheet of paper that contained a handwritten list. I read it with interest.

1) *Barnett is Miss A's solicitor.*
2) *Sanchez is a Central American trying to make his fortune in the citrus-growing industry.*
3) *Both men have some sort of design on Miss A, perhaps on others as well.*
4) *The exact nature of the connection between the two men is unknown.*
5) *Sanchez is a frequent guest of the Edisons, though neither husband nor wife appears to have any particular preferential fondness*

for him.

6) *Barnett has extensive ties to both England and North America, though none as-yet-discovered to Central America.*

7) *An ongoing investigation into Miss A's finances, conducted under the supervision of Mycroft Holmes, turns up nothing amiss, though some records cannot be accessed without her personal permission (or that of her solicitor, who is unaware of the investigation and might act in dangerous ways if provoked before he is fully captured). In addition, the finances of her American tour are not fully accounted-for as of yet.*

8) *Barnett represents many wealthy clients, and investigations have begun into the accounts of several of the more prominent, though no inconsistencies have been uncovered to date.*

9) *Sanchez is almost certain not to know what Miss A looks like; therefore, personal contact will not present unreasonable risk.*

10) *Once Miss A's physical safety is secured, the next phase of the case must include deeper infiltration into Fort Myers society.*

I read the list with interest, noting the mixture of Holmes's terse observations and expanded explanations for my benefit. 'I get the impression—I mean, do you suppose the implications of the threat to be wider than a crude plot by a solicitor against a wealthy client?' I asked, looking at my companion curiously.

'I think it likely, as does my brother,' he answered, his face in a cloud of grey smoke. 'A common criminal would have already betrayed himself in a thousand ways. If Barnett desired to steal, innumerable ways to do so exist before him. But he's been too careful. Why, too, did he include the man Sanchez? The whole thing reads differently from a petty crime.

'I must also ask, Bernard, how my brother-in-law (I nearly laughed aloud) came by the letter from our friend in the first place.'

'That, my dear Lavinia, is one of the more interesting facts of the case. A clerk by the name of Michael Morgan caught sight of the letter on his employer's desk right before it was posted. He thought the contents odd and mentioned them that evening when he visited his doctor for treatment of a chest cold. His doctor's name, you might have guessed, is one John Watson, a London physician of considerable reputation who recently lost his dear friend of several years. In the absence of this friend, the good doctor gave the information to the next-best source, his friend's brother, who acquired the letter after it had reached the intended recipient. Even I do not know how that was accomplished, except that Sanchez has recently been enjoying himself in New York, where Mycroft has several associates.'

'I begin to see why Dr Watson's company is sought by those who appear to run in such different circles from those frequented by most physicians,' I commented, thinking as I did so that the poor man must be enduring a mountain of grief, a monstrously unfair lot for one who had been so loyal.

Holmes grew quiet for a moment before muttering, 'At least he had the sense to take it to Mycroft and not try to investigate it himself.' I ventured to imagine that perhaps his thoughts echoed my own.

'This evening, you and I are to dine with Thomas and Mina Edison, along with various guests, at Seminole Lodge,' said Holmes, and the vision of the tangled dresses in my trunk burst into my mind unwelcome. I would have to try my mother's technique of hanging them in a steamy washroom, a trick I hadn't thought of in years. I didn't complain, however, too interested by the prospect of the dinner to be irritated.

'What character do you wish me to portray?' I asked. The list Holmes had shown me had reminded me that, though I might be a concerned party in the case, I was entering an investigation that had been going on for some time. I was far from overawed by the detective, but I respected his methods.

'One's own character is the easiest to project,' he answered. 'I must seem eager and naïve, but no such injunctions apply to you. In fact, it may prove more convincing for you to seem like the cleverer wife of a slightly foolish husband. As to specifics, draw out the evening's participants as much as you can. Your appearance should keep the task from being overwhelmingly difficult.' At the last line, I laughed out loud. Holmes refrained from comment, but an expression crossed his face that was as near mirth as I had ever seen him.

Chapter 4: Holmes

In many ways, the beginning of the case had proved frustrating for Holmes. The acquisition of the initial letter had been vastly and coincidentally helpful, to the point that he wondered if someone had intended Mycroft to see it. It hardly seemed likely that it had been intended for Sherlock himself, since all of London except, perhaps, a few of Moriarty's associates, thought his corpse was at the bottom of a Swiss waterfall, and anyone remaining in Moriarty's now-defunct organisation would have the incentive to keep quiet and low-key for their own sakes. Perhaps a law clerk had simply been especially conscientious and especially ill at the same time. At any rate, the letter was genuine, and that meant the threat was genuine, or at the very least, someone had intended Mycroft to think so.

Since the first information, breakthroughs had been difficult to come by. If only he'd been able to start the investigation in London, where Barnett resided and, more importantly, kept his offices, he would most likely have solved the case in the time he had already spent waiting for letters and telegrams from Mycroft about the progress of his associates and their slow, methodical efforts. Beginning the investigation in Florida, with the recipient of the letter rather than the originator of the scheme, was an entirely backward way to go about things, and Holmes hated illogic even more than he loved logic. Still, even if he could have been in London, with all its resources, he would have had a nearly impossible time enlisting the help of the woman who was seated next to him on the train from Orlando to Fort Myers, dozing in preparation for the work ahead.

She hadn't slept well; he had seen that the moment he'd entered the hotel in the guise of the coachman. Her vibrantly blue eyes had been ringed by dark shadows, her reflexes had been delayed, and her responses to spoken questions had been slightly slower than usual. He reminded himself, too, that her failure to recognise him had not entirely been a compliment to his abilities. He wondered if he had sprung things on her too quickly. He'd known much of the information she had related, but not the depth of unhappiness in her marriage. In the past, his quick perception had made him suspect that The Woman would not be happy in a traditional marriage, the kind he had suspected the ostentatious lawyer sought, but he had not had enough contact with the man to discover the true depths of his designs. Perhaps he'd been too quick to reveal the betrayal of one of her only remaining friends, but he shook his head in denial of the idea. If the intended victim had been himself, he'd have wanted to be told as quickly as possible so that he could assimilate the information and act accordingly. Irene, with her quick wit and systematic mind, wasn't so very different. No, he was sure she'd have wanted to know as soon as possible, even if the knowledge was distressing. Mrs Lavinia James was a formidable force, and he would not have wanted to be the one with designs on her, whatever they might be.

*　　　*　　　*

'The sun doesn't appear to realise it's autumn, Bernard,' Irene observed as the train pulled into the Fort Myers depot, if the dilapidated shack and tiny excuse for a platform could possibly warrant that name. Holmes helped his companion exit the locomotive, taking care to hold her hand gently and smile down at her like a benevolent stork. He was still wearing the driver's costume of the morning, though his bearing made it appear completely different than it had earlier. Still, he left his companion at the door to the grimy women's facilities as quickly as possible and went to the men's, which were unspeakably dirty. He emerged moments later, dressed in a hat and black coat befitting a gentleman of Bernard James's station, which he had retrieved from the depths of his trunk. He was a much neater and more efficient packer than his companion, and his clothing had not suffered much during the journey. He smoothed his collar and proceeded to find a cab to bring him and Irene to Mrs Stillwell's on Monroe Street, the boardinghouse where he had lodged since his arrival. The Woman joined him as he conversed with a quick-looking young man who loaded their two trunks onto his tiny wooden cart straightaway. 'Very efficient, Americans,' observed Holmes, half as himself and half as Bernard James.

'My dear, I think we must find a new home,' said Holmes as their cab bounced roughly down the street. 'You will hardly be comfortable in the humble accommodations that have served me these three weeks.'

'Not at all, Bernard, I will make do as I always have.' Irene took the opportunity to slip her hand into Holmes's with a sickeningly sweet look, which he acknowledged with a benign smile before giving her an amused sideways glance. He had noted with satisfaction that the driver's face as they entered the cab had clearly registered the opinion that Bernard James was vastly and undeservedly fortunate to have married such a beautiful wife, an impression he hoped would be repeated by everyone they met.

In his three weeks of residence, Holmes had become used to the tropical foliage that lined the road—the flowers that bloomed brightly in mid-autumn and the palm trees that shed large coconuts onto the roads. Someone even grew pineapple a few miles outside of town. He had always been affected by atmospheres. The hubbub of London was like a steady hum that called to him and told him secrets about its inner workings. Florida was different, almost silent, save for the growl of the animals that prowled the night-time. He couldn't feel a pulse nearly nonexistent underneath the beating sun, and the lack of bearings unsettled him. But she was here now—The Woman. Perhaps in talking to her, he would see a pattern emerge from the confusion.

*   *   *

Mina Edison was the first to greet Holmes that evening as he guided Irene into Seminole Lodge, the home Thomas Edison had commissioned for his family. It was a large white house, not opulent, but beautifully situated on grounds the inventor was already filling with the evidence of one of his many passions—botany. The sound of laughter echoed throughout the premises, and the lady of the house came forward quickly to greet her guests. At twenty-six, Mina Edison was a handsome woman in the height of good health, black-haired and sturdy. She was not a classic beauty, but Holmes thought he understood the middle-aged inventor's fascination with her when he saw the spark of intelligence and wit in her eyes.

'Good evening, Mr James,' she said with a friendly smile. 'I'm so pleased you've finally brought your wife.' Mina took in Irene, dressed in a long, demure blue gown, her chestnut hair piled atop her head, and her eyes widened.

'This is Lavinia,' said Holmes, pushing the perfect note of pride into his voice.

'Welcome to Seminole Lodge,' said Mina warmly, taking Irene by the hand. 'Let me introduce you. We're always happy to have new women down here. It evens the numbers against the male onslaught.' Holmes watched Irene smile shyly and laughed to himself. He doubted Irene Adler had ever had a shy moment in her life. 'I suppose you can come along, Mr James,' said Mina, looking back at him with a mildly teasing smile. Holmes rarely

46

had trouble creating rapport with any woman he chose, and Mina was no exception. It helped that he genuinely liked her.

Mina led them through to a large room with several simple wooden chairs, a white sofa, a grand piano, and a fireplace, something Holmes doubted the Edisons needed frequently, even in the dead of winter. On his first visit to the Lodge, he'd wondered why they had chosen to include it at all, but he had come to learn that Floridians were as enamored of old-world glamour as their northern counterparts, and that those who had come from New England were particularly likely to reproduce their northern comforts in their southern dwellings, whether they needed them or not. And yet, a hint of something different was also present in the light colours and relaxed furnishings, an acknowledgment of the coast and the sea, a curious mixture of familiar and tropical.

Holmes's eyes darted around the room, taking in the evening's participants. To his disappointment, Sanchez was not among the guests. Instead, he saw the inventor engaged in conversation with a short young man he didn't recognise. Another unfamiliar man, tall and broad-shouldered, stood to the side listening to the laugh of a loud, stout, middle-aged woman whom Holmes recognised as Jerusha McGregor, who went by 'Tootie.' He didn't blame her. Her husband Ambrose, a quiet, prudent businessman who seemed almost extraordinary in his averageness, spoke to Marion Edison, Thomas Edison's eldest child, a strong-willed, attractive eighteen-year-old who seemed to have inherited the bulk of her father's brains. At only eight years older than she, Mina Edison acted as a fond older sister, but was far from maternal. A small party, then, which was fortunate. Easier to draw out individuals with fewer from whom to choose.

Mina brought Irene to her husband, and Holmes followed obediently behind. 'Tom, this is Bernard's wife, Lavinia, whom we've heard so much about.' Edison's deafness wasn't apparent immediately; he was an excellent lip reader, and his speech was normal. Nevertheless, Holmes noted the way his wife turned toward him when she spoke and took care to enunciate her words clearly. Irene smiled demurely, and Edison greeted her politely. The younger man smiled very shyly and submitted to being introduced as Nelson Burroughs. 'I understand, Lavinia, that you are musical,' said Mina eagerly after pleasantries had been exchanged. 'I hope that after dinner, you will favour us with a song, if your journey hasn't tired you out too much.'

'Oh, I hope so too,' put in Tootie suddenly, wandering over. 'Marion plays, so it will be a huge treat for her.' Ambrose calmly followed in his wife's wake, and her conversational partner, the tall stranger, stood at the edge of the group, looking on without comment.

'Oh, Mr Murphy,' said Mina, turning toward him after a moment, 'I'm sorry I haven't done the honours. Our newcomers are Lavinia and Bernard James. This is Mr John Murphy of Montana, enjoying his first taste of south Floridian life.' The large man's voice was predictably booming as he greeted hostess and guests.

'No one's done the honours for us, either,' said Tootie once he had subsided, 'but we're quite capable of it ourselves. I'm Tootie McGregor, and this is my man himself, Ambrose.' Far from embarrassment, Ambrose McGregor seemed massively pleased to be possessed of such an outgoing wife. He smiled at Irene, who said her hellos in a quiet voice. 'My goodness, you're lovely,' said Tootie, taking a good look at her. 'And American. I've no wonder you chose one of those British men to marry. If our boys talked like that, this state would be far more populated.' Mina Edison looked vaguely horrified. Her stepdaughter, the only non-speaking participant remaining, appeared vastly amused.

To the relief of the hostess, a young maid came in just then to signal the beginning of dinner. Holmes held his arm out for Irene, who took it and seemed relieved—whether genuinely or not, he was unsure. 'I'm afraid I must insist on taking my own wife through, Mrs Edison. Our time apart has been most

49

distressing,' he explained, with a benign smile at their hostess. Marion Edison made her own introduction of herself to Irene on the way to the dining room, smiling in a genuinely friendly way before taking the arm of the Montana cattleman. Holmes wondered what age the others ascribed to Irene. She looked younger than her thirty-two years, though she could also look older. Mina seemed to regard her as an equal, which was fortunate under the circumstances.

Holmes's wish for the evening would have been to take on the inventor, to listen to Thomas Edison and exchange ideas with his brilliant mind, but Bernard James did not have such capacities. Instead, his real objective was to draw out Tootie McGregor and her husband, whom he had only met once before in a larger party. They were prominent in south Floridian society and undoubtedly knew the business of everyone in town. The wife hardly seemed like a difficult subject for such a task, though he was less sure about her quiet husband. Burroughs, too, was an unknown quantity, though any connection to a plot between an English solicitor and a Central American entrepreneur seemed farfetched at best. Nevertheless, Holmes kept his eyes on everyone.

Chapter 5: Irene

I was nervous, I'll confess, as I took my seat at the large dining table. Holmes had spent the afternoon briefing me and then quizzing me about the details of the lives of Bernard and Lavinia James, and I had dutifully learned locations and dates and pleasing filial anecdotes. But facts, even emotionally affecting ones, are far from the reality of taking on a character. Holmes had assured me I could behave as myself, but at the same time I was strongly aware of the fact that Lavinia James was far from Irene Adler in her experiences and habits. In addition to this, I would also be required to concentrate on the others in the situation, some of whom Holmes would have met, but all of whom would be strangers to me. Once or twice, I nearly told Holmes to continue the investigation if he liked, but to consider himself divorced from the unfortunate Lavinia, who wished to return instead to her much less complicated life as the celebrated contralto Irene Adler. Each time, one look at Holmes's provoking face steeled my resolve. The *great detective* might be wildly skilled at this sort of thing, taking roles and probing for information as easy to him as breathing air, but it was new to me, and I would not give him the satisfaction of seeing me give up. If he believed I could successfully pull it off, I would do more than that; I would be magnificent.

The beginning of the evening had asked little of me in terms of conversation or activity, so my nerves were on edge when I looked up to find that John Murphy, the mild mannered cattleman, was to my right. Ambrose McGregor was on my left, but he had already been forcibly engaged in conversation with his wife and the young Burroughs on the way into the dining room. He would have to be left until a lull, which I doubted would ever occur where Tootie was involved, or for after dinner, when Holmes might engage the men separately.

I took a sip of the beverage in front of me and nearly coughed. It was Coca-Cola, an impossibly sweet, fizzy beverage America had produced during my time in England. Mistaking my expression as one of enthusiasm, Marion Edison, who was next to Holmes across the table, eagerly declared, 'They say they'll be selling it in bottles any day now, but Papa has it brought in from the drugstore for parties.' I couldn't help enjoying her excitement, though I'd have much preferred a glass of wine. Holmes had warned me not to expect the spirits to flow freely, as Mina Edison was a devout Methodist, her husband also held to Methodist teaching, and both were staunchly opposed to the consumption of strong drink of any kind. I smiled politely, and Marion beamed. I appeared to have unintentionally passed some sort of test in her eyes. All the better, I thought. Young people often have open ears and the benefit of not awakening others' suspicions. At eighteen, I had known plenty of things with the potential to embarrass any number of other people. I thought I might find out what sorts of things Marion knew.

The first course included a large green gelatin mould containing all kinds of fruit, and the conversation for a time was taken up with admiring it and with Tootie's insistence that Mina's cook should give her the recipe for her cook, who lacked the proper finesse in preparing such creations. Mina dutifully (and, I thought, with some measure of amusement) offered her cook's services for lessons at any time. In my view, the modern craze for outlandish gelatin was ridiculous. It would have been one thing if the stuff tasted good, but it was horrid. The pile of sticky, indifferent fruit that ended up on my plate reminded me of the one thing I missed about my life in Yorkshire—the plain, unfussy cooking that still predominated in the English countryside. But I soldiered on and managed to fit in a comment about the superiority of American cooks' mastery of the dish.

After a few minutes, the men began to grow restless, and Murphy asked Edison what he was working on. The inventor's eyes lit up at this, and my own interest increased. Everyone else at the table, even the loquacious Tootie, grew silent out of respect for the man. 'I will show you all the new Kinetoscope tonight, if the ladies won't mind the laboratory,' he said deferentially. Several enthusiastic heads nodded, and Mina looked toward those of us who were newcomers.

'Tom means the new motion-picture device he's been working on. It's terribly clever.' She smiled sweetly at her husband and touched his hand lightly, which brought forth an answering smile from the inventor. 'The best explanation will be seeing it for yourselves, I think,' Mina continued, and I saw that Edison seemed disappointed not to be able to elaborate further.

As the meal progressed, conversation became less formal and more diverse, and I finally found myself able to engage Murphy in conversation over the main course of oyster stew. 'I understand that you are from Montana, Mr Murphy,' I began, watching as he nearly knocked his delicate china bowl off the table. 'I have never been so far West. I was born in New Jersey, and I have spent all my time in the United States on the East Coast. I must ask if the stories of street shootouts and wild Indians are as common as we're told.' I wiped my lips daintily on my napkin, priding myself that my inane question was exactly the sort of thing Lavinia James could be expected to wonder.

Murphy smiled broadly and began speaking in a tone of voice that would have worked marvellously if he'd been addressing a ten-year-old child. 'Now, Mrs James, you fine ladies with your novels mustn't assume we're all uncivilised. Most of my business is done in banks and offices, and I have employees just like the offices back East do.' He leaned closer to me. 'Of course, if there's the occasional bit of trouble, we know what to do.' His eyes twinkled, but I wondered exactly what sort of *trouble* he might actually have encountered and whether or not it extended to south Florida. He seemed a laid-back man, but there was a feeling of steel behind his good humour that I wouldn't have wanted to test. I saw that Holmes, while he was engaged in charming Marion, had also been listening, and I wondered what he had gleaned from the interaction that I might have missed.

Dinner was uneventful after that, finishing with brownies, an American dessert that resembled a chocolate cake with the consistency of a plum pudding. I thought it the best part of the meal. Drawing people out over food was more difficult than I'd expected, especially without alcoholic beverages to lower the barriers of the diners. I determined to try harder as the evening progressed. Holmes smiled at me, his face angular in the electric lights against the shadows of falling dusk.

'We should wait for sunset to see the Kinetoscope,' said Mina as we took the last sips of our coffee. 'It's marvellous in the dark.'

'Let's have music until then,' Tootie put in loudly, grinning with chocolate-stained teeth. 'I can't wait to hear Lavinia. If she's half as good as Bernard claimed last time, we'll all be in tears.' I looked over at Holmes, who was staring innocently at the floral wallpaper. He hadn't ever heard me sing before the last time he'd dined with the Edisons and their guests, at least as far as I knew. Impossible man.

Mina seamlessly moved her guests back into the piano room, where the ambiance was pensive in the half light. She gently motioned to the instrument as the others sat down on the sofa and chairs. Nelson Burroughs took the chair closest to the instrument and seemed to be excited at the prospect of the music, the most emotion he'd shown all evening. I wondered if he was a musician himself.

I sat down and began to play, opening with a medium-tempo dance tune. I watched my audience and, as usual, they began to relax as the music soothed them. My second song was a light comic number, a favourite from my time in England before my wedding. Finally, when I had their attention, I went to the popular love song that was the climax of each of my concerts.

I studied them all as I sang. Holmes, in the guise of Bernard, looked enchanted. Mina was surprised and pleased, I believe, having doubted the glowing praise of a husband. Marion seemed slightly bewildered, as if the music pleased her and invaded her at the same time. I felt a pang of sorrow for the inventor until I realised that his hand on the edge of the piano allowed him to experience its vibrations. Burroughs was as into the music as I'd expected, keeping slow time on his knee. The Montanan was quiet and, I thought, the least under the spell. Tootie was wide-eyed and vocal, making unintelligible delighted noises, while her husband smiled kindly and looked as if his mind was far away. I looked back to Holmes at last, wondering if his admiration belonged to Bernard after all, or if any part of it belonged to Sherlock Holmes, Consulting Detective.

After I finished playing, everyone sat quietly for a moment, even Tootie, her face wet with tears as she held her husband's hand. Finally, Mina broke the silence. 'Thank you so much, Mrs James. We're fortunate to have heard that.' I couldn't help feeling pleased. She turned to her husband. 'Now, Tom dear, I think it's time!'

The inventor smiled dramatically and arose, and everyone else followed. He took a lantern from atop a shelf and led us out into the now-black nighttime. The lantern illuminated a well-worn path from the house to a smaller building, a path lined with shrubs and bright flowers I did not recognise, no doubt part of the inventor's collection. Edison opened a creaky door and with the flip of a switch immediately flooded the laboratory with electric light. Our eyes squinted in shock at the contrast between the brightness inside and the darkness of the grounds.

The laboratory was large and rectangular, lined with wooden shelves and with tables covered in all manner of glassware in rows down its centre. I wondered whimsically if the organised pandemonium resembled the inventor's mind.

Edison went immediately to work setting up a large machine made of metal and wood, his wife by his side assisting him at every turn. Clearly, Mina Edison was well-versed in her husband's endeavours. While we waited, Marion amused Tootie by listing for her the names of various chemicals that stood in unmarked bottles on the shelves around the walls. I listened with amazement as the girl explained that her father had all the names stored in his memory, as did his assistants, making labelling unnecessary. Holmes stood at one end of the room, the very picture of affable confusion, engaging Murphy in meaningless conversation about how grand it all was. Ambrose and Burroughs stood apart, watching silently.

Finally, after several moments of congenial work by the Edisons and less successful attempts by their guests to entertain themselves in a room in which they could safely touch nothing, Mina motioned us all to her husband's side, in front of the large brown contraption. 'Stay here,' she said quietly. 'We're going to switch off the lights, and you'll be able to see it one-by-one. Stand in line just here.' The men deemed it sporting to let the ladies go first, but the ladies in turn demurred, and so we ended up in a cluster rather than a line, with Burroughs finally nervously volunteering to begin. Mina brought him toward a box she and her husband had assembled at the front of the contraption, and then the room went black.

I realised a moment later that Edison had turned off the electric bulbs, a characteristically dramatic move, leaving us in the darkness of the evening. Someone swore under his breath, Murphy, I thought, and Tootie let out a slight shriek before everyone fell silent. 'That's cracking good, Edison!' was the next audible noise, spoken, of course, by Burroughs, who had apparently forgotten his host's deafness. In a moment, I heard the almost imperceptible sound of one hand lightly striking another—Mina Edison translating the words into Morse Code for the benefit of her husband. Holmes had told me that they often communicated in that way.

The lights were again blinding as Burroughs finished and came back to join the group, his face transformed by a wide, unselfconscious grin. He refused to breathe a word of the machine, and the next volunteer was Tootie, who took her place at the box while we all braced ourselves for the lights to disappear. This time, we took it better, a few of us even managing to chuckle; however, I nearly screamed when I felt a hand touch my arm and heard a low voice whisper, 'I must have a, word with you, Mrs James.' I forced my brain to place the voice as that of Ambrose McGregor.

'Later,' I breathed, glad for Tootie's frequent exclamations of delight at whatever the contraption did. I felt chilled to the bone, even in the warm weather. Of all the people present, I hadn't expected Ambrose to be the mystery. There had been something so kind in his quiet appreciation of his wife and his dinner that I hardly knew what to think. Was it possible the man fancied me? I put the thought out of my mind as preposterous (I hoped) and began to conceive of a plan to speak with him alone. When the lights came back on, I stole a look at his face, but he did not even glance in my direction.

My preoccupation consumed me to the point that I hardly cared when Marion finally pushed me forward for my turn at the machine. I bent down according to Mina's whispered instructions and looked into a hole the size of a silver dollar as the lights went out. Before my eyes was a still picture of a boxer with his fist raised to strike. As I watched, the picture began to move, and the man landed the punch squarely on his opponent's jaw. For thirty seconds I watched, open-mouthed, as a professional boxing match took place before my eyes. I was still hunched over, marveling, when the laboratory came back to life. I looked gratefully for the face of the inventor and enunciated as best I could, 'I'm absolutely stunned, Mr Edison. I've never seen anything like it.' His serious face broke into a smile, and I believe he'd have shown us all again if his wife hadn't stopped him with a small shake of her dark head.

I had been the last of the guests to view the Kinetoscope, so my viewing was followed by Edison and Mina putting the machine away in a cabinet in the corner of the laboratory. This time, everyone lingered nearby, hoping that by watching the Kinetoscope's dismantling, they might somehow understand its mechanism. I moved slowly toward Holmes, and he sensed my object and moved into a corner of the room, between a table and a large grey cabinet. Without warning, he hooked a long arm around my waist and pulled me close, whispering in my ear. 'I heard Ambrose McGregor speak during the blackout, but I could not understand what he said. Was I correct in assuming he addressed you?' I leaned into him like the most enamored of wives.

'He requested a private discussion with me. I intend to lose one of my gloves here and discover the loss once we reach the house. I will require a gentleman to walk me back, but you will be engaged elsewhere.' Holmes nodded once as Tootie's voice cut into our tête-à-tête.

'My goodness, look at those lovebirds. It's no wonder, since they've been separated.' Her blonde head bobbed in delight.

'Please excuse my enthusiasm, Mrs Edison,' said Holmes with a gallant near-bow. 'I fear my wife's return and your husband's grand machine have made me quite giddy.' I smiled sheepishly, clinging to his hand.

Mina smiled indulgently. 'I'm sure we're all delighted to have met your charming wife, Mr James.' The guests nodded as one, and I felt a pang of genuine pleasure.

The party's return to the house was almost festive, but dread lay at the bottom of my stomach like a lead weight. Whatever Ambrose McGregor had to say, I highly doubted it was anything I would be overly excited to hear.

When we reached the piano room, Burroughs began to declare his intention of leaving, and Murphy looked ready to follow suit. Before Mina could begin her polite farewells, I made a show of looking down at my hands and finding one gloved and the other bare. At the same moment, Holmes asked Tootie about her favourite topic—her chronically ill son Bradford. He stopped mid-sentence when I lamented, 'Oh no, I've been terribly clumsy. I seem to have lost my glove on the way back.'

'Don't worry, dear, Tom can go and retrieve it,' said Mina kindly, putting a hand on my arm.

'Nonsense,' I answered, 'your husband has been far too kind already this evening. Perhaps my husband—,' but Bernard James looked down at Tootie with the crestfallen expression of a man disappointed at being unable to hear the words ready to fall from her lips. Bless her, she took the bait.

'Ambrose, you can take her,' she said brightly. 'I was just about to tell Mr James about Bradford's ailment.' Her husband nodded wordlessly and proffered his arm to me, using the other to pick up the lantern from the shelf where Edison had placed it.

'Thank you so much!' I said, trying to project artlessly breathless gratitude. Tootie fairly beamed upon me, and I fancied she had decided to take me on as a sort of protégé.

We were halfway between the house and the laboratory before Ambrose spoke. 'Mrs James,' he said quietly, 'I hope you don't think me impertinent. I wish to say at the outset that I mean you no harm.'

'I was sure of it, Mr McGregor,' I rejoined, supposing it to be the sort of thing Lavinia might say, though it was a blatant lie in the mouth of Irene Adler.

'The truth is—,' we reached the door of the laboratory building, and he opened it, shining the lantern inside. I walked quickly toward the side of the room where I had placed my glove. 'The truth is, Mrs James, that I believe you may be in grave danger.'

'Excuse me?' I said, turning around to face the man, his plain face hardly visible in the shadows the lantern cast against the dark walls.

'This is hard to say,' he continued in a slow, stuttering voice, 'but I have reason to believe your husband is not who he claims to be.' I froze. Of all the possibilities I had considered, this contingency had never crossed even the furthest recess of my mind.

'Whatever do you mean, Sir?' I asked in my most husband-defending tone, moving back outside where the moonlight cast less garish light. Ambrose's expression was filled with pained concern.

'I have reason to believe that the gentleman who claims to be Bernard James is actually an English detective by the name of Sherlock Holmes.' I nearly laughed. Only by the immediate application of a pinch to my forearm was I able to keep from making noise. I thought quickly. Holmes and I had not discussed this situation. I was sure that the detective, with his seemingly omniscient mind, must have considered it, but he had most likely dismissed it as a near-impossibility.

Ambrose continued in the midst of my silence. 'There is a man who lives in town by the name of Sanchez, and he—well, he is more acquainted with the ways of this person than I am. I first met your husband at this house during a large party a week ago, and Sanchez was also a guest. He took me aside that night and told me he had spotted Holmes, who, I gather, is somehow affiliated with the police. At the time, Sanchez voiced his opinion that the ruse was most likely harmless. After all, the man's reputation is as a champion of good. I could not, however, fail to speak when I realised that you, his wife, seem unaware of his true identity. I am sorry if I have caused you distress, but I could not bear to stand by and watch a lady as fine as yourself be taken in.'

I looked up into the kind, concerned face of Ambrose McGregor, and I made a decision. I am generally a good judge of character. Barring the blinders that caused me to marry a monster, I am rarely ever wrong. I wondered briefly what Holmes would wish me to do, but I was in a bind, pinned to the wall like a lab specimen. I had the choice of trying to come up with some wildly elaborate ruse to fool a seemingly reasonable man, or else come out with the truth and trust his judgement and good will. I chose the latter.

'Mr McGregor,' I said, standing close to him in the lantern light, 'I will be quick, or the others will wonder what is keeping us. The things you say are true, and if you will call on us tomorrow at Mrs Stillwell's boardinghouse, we will explain them to you. I ask you, as a personal favour, to please trust me and keep silent about this until then.' The pleading look I gave him was unfeigned.

'You're quite a woman, Mrs James,' was all he said as he turned back toward the house.

Chapter 6: Holmes

The moment Irene entered the house on the arm of Ambrose McGregor, Holmes could tell something had seriously rattled her, which he hadn't expected. With sudden horror, he wondered if the older man had bothered her in some personal way. The detective's eyes searched her keenly, but Irene's smile and enthusiastic thanks seemed to convince the others, at least, that all was well. Mercifully, goodbyes were soon said, and within minutes he had his companion settled into a hired runabout. It was hardly elegant, but carriages were hard to come by in Fort Myers. As soon as he had handed Irene up, he retrieved a blanket from the floor behind, tucking it around her knees like a solicitous husband might.

'I'm quite warm enough, Bernard,' she said

calmly, though none of the others were around to hear. Holmes hopped up beside her and studied her face, trying to ascertain her state of mind, punishing himself mentally for allowing her to go unaccompanied into danger, but she remained quiet, and her face remained impassive until they reached Mrs Stillwell's house.

Holmes willed his hands to be especially gentle as he helped Irene down from the carriage. She was small, he realised. He had never considered it, not properly, not as anything more than a statistical fact. The prints her feet made in the dirt pathway to the back door were tiny, practically a child's prints. Why, oh why, had he been foolish enough to send her off alone with the man? His mind, the fallible organ to which he attached such trust, had painted a picture of The Woman as a force, a tower of strength. He now realised that she was both more and less than that, and he cursed himself inwardly for his lack of concern.

As they mounted the stairs to his room at Mrs Stillwell's, Holmes's hand hovered in the vicinity of Irene's elbow in case she should lose her footing. He did not touch her. She still remained speechless, and he wondered if he would have to employ some unusual method to cause her to explain the encounter. He knew that wronged women were often loathe to speak of their experiences for days or even weeks, and some, he had heard, even refused to speak at all. He could not afford for her to be one of those.

The proprietress of the house was prodigiously proud of having electricity and of living so near the inventor of the lightbulb himself, as she had eagerly told Holmes upon his arrival, and she charged dearly for both. The detective turned on the prized electric light as soon as he and Irene had entered the worn upstairs room, and he watched his companion remove her hat and wash her hands in the basin. Having finished, she turned and looked him full in the face.

'My goodness, Holmes, you look as if you've seen a spectre.' The detective sat down in the lone wooden chair and watched her, puzzled. 'Since you have not asked me the content of my conversation with Ambrose McGregor, I can only assume you thought it as prudent as I did to wait until we were privately secluded.' As she spoke, Irene sat down on the edge of the uncomfortable bed and unpinned her chestnut hair, letting it fall in waves down her back. Holmes supposed that she felt no shame in this, since, after all, the man before her had once seen her dressed as a young man.

'I hope very much that you will not blame me, Holmes.' Her eyes pleaded with him, though he saw no evidence of personal injury or offense and began to conclude that his original assessment of her distress had been mistakenly reasoned. 'McGregor's aim and purpose was to save me from the unfortunate fate of a deceived woman. In short, Holmes, he went through all that trouble to tell me that my husband was none other than the famed English detective Sherlock Holmes.'

At this, Sherlock Holmes of Baker Street, consulting detective to queen and country, threw back his head and laughed, but The Woman did not join him. 'Believe me, Holmes,' she continued when he had subsided, 'my initial inclination was the same as yours, but the knowledge of Ambrose's source distressed me more than his disclosure amused me. Alberto Sanchez somehow recognised you last week.' Holmes nodded, not entirely surprised. Sanchez was the only one with a likely connection. The detective did not yet know exactly what it was or to what it tended, but it would have been almost insupportably coincidental for any person wholly unconnected to the case to have recognised him. Barnett had been more thorough than even Holmes had expected.

'Ambrose said Sanchez called your deception harmless.'

'Interesting,' said Holmes, pulling a well-worn notebook and pen from his black leather travelling case. 'Let us evaluate where this places us. First, I believe we may almost certainly rule out the idea that Ambrose McGregor is lying.'

'The thought had occurred to me,' murmured Irene, 'but I could not think of a reasonable motive, and he gave no appearance of it.'

'Well, we may keep the possibility as a remote contingency to fall back on if no other roads lead us to fruitful enquiry, but I doubt it will be needed. Second, we know that Sanchez knows my appearance and is aware that I am alive. This leads to the question: Was Sanchez warned of my continuing existence before and told to be on the lookout for my presence, or was his recognition of me an accident? If the first, then we may suppose a network of people is aware that I am alive; if the second, Sanchez may know of me by some other means, such as a photo of me with someone else whom he has been taught to recognise. I have had few photos taken, but unfortunately some do exist at the cajoling of Watson and Inspector Lestrade of Scotland Yard. Third, where does your solicitor, Barnett, fit into the equation? If he is aware that I am alive, why has he not had me tailed? I can say with certainty that I have not been followed since my arrival in America. As improbable as it may seem, I begin to lean toward the possibility that Sanchez may have recognised me by near-chance. There is one particular photo that appeared in the *London Times* some years ago, after I had helped a certain peer regain a necklace stolen from his wife by a famous jewel thief. My work resulted

70

in the man being caught and imprisoned, not only for the theft in question, but also for several other previously unsolved cases. The picture was notable because it contained the likenesses of several officers of Scotland Yard, Dr Watson, myself, and, most unusually, my brother Mycroft, who had been persuaded to pose for it by the prime minister, who wished the government to receive positive publicity from the incident. The photo's presence in a prominent newspaper means that numerous reproductions of it were produced, and any number of individuals might have procured it easily.'

Holmes leaned forward and gazed intently into The Woman's attentive face. 'I wonder, Irene, what part Mycroft was intended to play in all of this. As I told you, the letter from Barnett to Sanchez came to him with almost serendipitous chance. I wonder now, more than ever, if my brother was meant to be involved. Perhaps the mastermind, whether Barnett, Sanchez, or someone else, misjudged his character and believed that he would take up where his younger brother had left off— with the same sort of investigation. Perhaps Sanchez was taught to expect to see the face of the elder brother, but instead found himself surprisingly face-to-face with the younger.'

'But for what purpose could he possibly need to know your brother's face?'

'That is what we must find out. I am afraid,

Irene, that this will be our last taste of fine accommodations for some time. Tonight, Bernard and Lavinia James will receive urgent news that calls them back home to England. Tomorrow, you and I will emerge as merchants to set up shop among the migrant day labourers, our faces different enough to fool even those we met this evening if necessary. We may safely hope that our roles will not be tested too acutely right away, for I intend us to mix with a segment of local society that families like the Edisons are hardly likely to meet on a regular basis.'

Holmes noted that Irene's eyes held excitement rather than fear and trust rather than suspicion. Her beautiful face was alive with the prospect of adventure. 'Tell me what you wish me to do, and I will help in any way I can.'

'First,' he said quietly, 'I must thank you for your cool head this evening. Without you, I would be in grave danger with no idea of my own peril. Second, it is obvious that both of us take a great risk by remaining here. I now believe, much more than at any previous point in this case, that the key to the mystery may be found here, but that very fact means harm is not far away. If you wish to extricate yourself, I will not deter you.'

Irene put out a small hand and lightly touched the detective's long fingers as they rested on his knee. 'I agreed to help you,' she said softly, 'and I will continue to do so as long as I may be useful. I assure you, I am not afraid.' Just then, out of nowhere, she smiled—a rare, wide, bracing smile. Holmes returned it with one of his own. They spent the rest of the night preparing to take on new characters.

The next morning, Gloria Stillwell rose to find on her front hall table a generous sum of money and a note explaining that Mr and Mrs Bernard James had been forced to return to England at their earliest possible convenience to care for a sick friend. Meanwhile, a tall man and a short man dressed in cheap clothing visited the poorest section of Fort Myers and hired an elderly horse and nearly-defunct wagon, which they filled with tattered raiment and low-quality goods. Their afternoon enquiry into the rental of a tiny, empty shop with a dilapidated sign that had once read 'Sloane's General Store' proved rewarding, and a few more cartfuls of goods meant that Sherlock Holmes and Irene Adler were in business by evening, proud occupants of a small, square building with sandy floors, empty shelves, and nothing to recommend it except its location and the miniscule flat above it.

The following morning, Holmes dressed himself after a long sleepless night spent in one of the spindly chairs the previous occupants had seen fit to leave in the tattered flat, his pipe forming a pleasant accompaniment to the slight coolness in the evening breeze. Irene had slept soundly, no doubt exhausted from the previous night's sleeplessness and the previous day's transactions. One day was hardly long enough to rent and stock a general store, but that name was generous in this case, and Holmes meant it to be. Forced to be unrecognisable in high society, he intended to work from within another strata of the infrastructure that kept the city moving, that of the migrant day labourers, of whom Alberto Sanchez employed three hundred in his citrus grove on the outskirts of town. If Holmes could not get at the man directly, he would work through his organisation. The stakes were higher now. If Sanchez knew his face and knew that he lived, Holmes could not afford to rest.

Once dressed in coarse brown slacks and a slightly ill-fitting grey shirt, Holmes darkened his skin and altered his face, making himself appear weathered and inelegant. He added wrinkles and rounded his sharp features. The cracked mirror on one of the walls revealed him as a middle-aged workman, which was exactly what he desired. He intended that that anyone entering the store should think him a manual labourer whose ambitions had acquired him a dingy store of his own.

After finishing his own toilette, he woke Irene with a gentle shake to the shoulder before leaving the room to give her time to dress. She had been dressed as a male the previous day, but from now on she would portray the lady of the establishment, a woman slightly nearer gentility than her husband, but still coarse and weatherbeaten. Holmes reentered the room upon hearing a light tap from inside the door. Irene wore a plain yellow cotton dress, worn from its previous owner's use, but she was still stunningly beautiful. Wordlessly, Holmes placed the rickety chair in front of the basin and began to work on his still-sleepy companion, using makeup to create lines of exhaustion and worry where there were none and slight asymmetry in near-perfect features. At last, he took her hair and mussed it slightly, arranging it as sloppily as he could without arriving at a completely inappropriate conclusion. He took care to commit every step to memory so that he would be able to replicate the results as many times as needed.

Irene walked over to the broken mirror and stared at her reflection. 'I'm afraid I can't completely eradicate your beauty without more extensive work,' murmured Holmes behind her, in a tone laced with irony.

'Don't worry,' she said, whirling on him. 'Godfrey couldn't manage it either, no matter how hard he tried.'

The tall detective stepped back as if he'd been slapped, but regained his composure after a moment. 'I've found us a place to eat breakfast before we open.' He spoke as if nothing had happened, but Irene wouldn't look at him. Without speaking further, he led the way downstairs and into the morning half-light of the dusty road.

Barcroft's wasn't the sort of place Lavinia and Bernard James would visit, but it was every bit the kind of place Jane and Tom Perkins, junk and supply store owners, would certainly frequent. Holmes and Irene were ushered into the cramped establishment and seated at a round table in a tiny, dubiously-kept corner, away from the few groups of working-class men who had come in for a very early-morning breakfast and, for some, liquid fortification. The other patrons' initial glances at the newcomers gave way to disinterest, so the detective was assured that their disguises were at least marginally effective. Holmes took a sip of the indifferent coffee the waitress brought and declared it vile with a disgusted expression. Irene looked up and met his gaze, then dropped her eyes quickly. 'This will not do,' he murmured, whether to himself or to her he was unsure. It had been a great deal of time since he'd had such protracted contact with a female of any sort, and he was beginning to recall the pitfalls that invariably complicated such associations. Watson had his days, of course, but a glass of scotch and a good pork pie set him to rights without difficulty. One couldn't ply Irene Adler with a pork pie and expect the same result, more was the pity. The detective's mind extended to the furthest bounds of male existence, but where females were concerned, there had always been certain blanks. The current problem was that communication, which was vital during a case, required the cooperation of two, and one of those two was persisting in her silence.

'I apologise, Holmes.' The Woman's voice interrupted his thoughts. 'I have no cause to bring my private feelings into the case.' Holmes stared at her as if she had suddenly acquired the power of speech after profound muteness.

'Ah,' he said.

'Quite,' she replied, blushing and staring at the thick white plate on the table before her. Holmes felt fortunate when a plate of irregularly-shaped sausage arrived a moment later, accompanied by white pillows of dough the waitress called biscuits, though they were nothing like the English variety.

'Don't you intend to eat?' Irene asked once she had taken a few bites and noticed his lack of movement.

'Not hungry,' Holmes answered. 'I rarely require food while I work.'

'Well, that's one difference between us,' his companion replied between bites, her good humour apparently restored. The biscuits seemed to meet with her approval, as she downed three of them and two large sausages. 'I always eat well when I'm on tour,' she continued after she had finished her last crumb. 'Otherwise, I'm inclined toward irritation.' Holmes caught a mischievous glint in her eye.

Watson might be easier to handle, but he was hardly given to mischievous glances.

Chapter 7: Irene

I found, after breakfast, that I looked forward to the day. The sense of impending danger was not entirely absent from my mind, but my unfamiliar clothing and the paint on my face gave me a measure of freedom I had not enjoyed while still in my own guise. I would have to be more vigilant, I realised, not to allow myself to strike at Holmes for being the only available representative of the non-female species. The detective hardly deserved that, and any debt he owed me from our previous skirmish he had more than paid by taking the case.

We returned to the shop shoulder-to-shoulder, and Holmes briefed me on the objectives of the day. For the first time, we were to separate. He intended to visit the site of Sanchez's citrus grove, while I tended the store and learned what I could from anyone I met. Rather than being a cause for apprehension, the idea of being on my own invigorated me.

The idea of it invigorated me, that is. I was less thrilled when no one had come into the store after two hours and I had checked the sign for the third time. I decided to do some reconnaissance on the rest of the street, keeping an eye on the unprepossessing space where Holmes and I plied our temporary wares. My object was the store we had visited the previous day to purchase our ragged clothing, a well-kept secondhand shop with a matriarchal owner who considered herself far above her clientele. On our first visit, I'd been dressed as a boy, and I hadn't spoken. As a result, I hoped and expected that she wouldn't recognise me in my current incarnation.

A doorbell announced my entrance, and I was surprised to find a young man behind the counter instead of an elderly woman. 'Good morning, ma'am,' he said, his voice thick with the slow drawl of the American Deep South, and I acknowledged his greeting with a nod. I moved quickly through the main room, which held glass cases that cradled expensive items such as silver spoons and brooches of dubious origin, and passed through to a cluttered side room that held clothing racks, piles of dilapidated shoes, and hats stacked high on top of one another. For several minutes, I was the only patron in the store, but my waiting was finally rewarded by the entrance of a woman I watched her surreptitiously, ostensibly holding up a threadbare coat to test its suitability. She held a baby in one arm, nearly a newborn by the look of it, and her face was worn, though I thought she was no older than I was, if as old.

I listened casually as she began to address the youthful shopkeeper. 'Tommy, you better be glad you ain't out today. Bill's gone crazy cause Sanchez is in some kind of hurry to get it all in before the end of the month.' At the name Sanchez, I stopped moving and listened intently.

'What for?' asked the boy in a conspiratorial tone.

'Dunno,' was the disappointing answer, 'but my Jim says Bill's in a temper and screaming at everybody.' I took note. Even if this was the only thing I learned all day, at least I had something to tell Holmes. After the woman had left, I bought a pair of shoes with worn-out soles and departed with a word to the young man about the store I'd just opened with my husband. I walked back toward Sloane's General Store, not overly concerned at the prospect that someone might have stolen some of our cheap wares. On my way, I watched the sun's glare in shop windows and discerned nothing important or significant to the case.

Fortunately, the woman from the secondhand store stepped into the store right after me, balancing her tiny baby on her hip and holding a bag of purchases in her other hand. She stared at the cheap cookware, used furnishings, and non-perishable foods that lined the shelves almost haphazardly, picking up a jar of crushed sage. After a while, she brought it to the counter and asked me its price. In order to loosen her tongue, I quoted her an amount much lower than its value.

'You're new in town,' she said, with a slight air of distrust. 'I saw you in Morgan's just now.'

'That's right,' I said. 'My husband and I just came here from Iowa.'

'Well, you're lucky not to be in the groves.'

'Why is that?' I asked as nonchalantly as possible.

'Things are getting worse these days. My husband Jim went to work for a new boss because the pay is better, but it looks like he's going to force us all out in the end. It's the deadlines—most of the bosses'll need pickers for at least another four weeks, but he wants it all by the end of the month—only two weeks— and that means the foremen drive the men like slaves.'

'I'm terribly sorry,' I said sympathetically.

'Well, it's the way of this life,' she said, giving me a few coins and leaving.

*   *   *

I was vastly relieved when Holmes finally stepped through the door of the shop, looking

81

pleased. 'I can see that your day has proved more successful than mine,' I said by way of a greeting.

'Indeed,' he answered, locking the door and leading the way up the narrow, rickety stairs to the tiny upstairs flat. As we cleaned our faces, he began his story.

'My first object was Sanchez's citrus grove outside of town. I was admitted after a wheedling promise that my shop might be able to stock necessaries like tobacco and liquor at lower-than-market prices. Almost as soon as I stepped onto the premises, I learned a vital piece of information.'

'Sanchez is forcing the men to work much more quickly than the other growers' men,' I inserted.

'Exactly so,' said Holmes, looking gratifyingly surprised.

'I was introduced to an unpleasant character called Bill, who brought me into his office.'

'The foreman,' I put in, but Holmes ignored me this time.

'I was given to understand that a company office exists somewhere in town, but the field office is in a shed on the edge of the grove itself. I did not expect to be treated well enough to be introduced to the head foreman, and when I was, I began to be concerned that Sanchez himself might be in evidence, a possibility I would like to avoid for the moment. Thankfully, Bill mentioned offhand that his employer would be conducting business in town all day.

'But here's the rub, Irene,' he said, stopping dramatically as he finished wiping off the remnants of his altered nose. *The photograph was on his desk.* There I was, having a normal conversation, if somewhat dishonest in the common way, about cost and supply, with a picture of myself and my brother staring up at me. The man did not appear to recognise me, but I confess I was not entirely comfortable with the situation. The other odd thing is—' and he fixed his eyes on my now-clean face with intensity, 'the photo wasn't the one I predicted. I was wrong. It was one from several years ago, a picture of my brother and me on the day of my graduation from Cambridge. I was not aware a copy existed, other than the ones Mycroft and I possess.'

'How long has it been since you looked at that photograph, Holmes?' I asked quickly, feeling myself start to blush.

He shook his head. 'Not since the day I received it in a letter from my brother three months after the occasion. Since then, it has resided among my personal papers.' I stood with my back to him, trying to will my face back to its usual colour.

'Do you remember when Mrs Hudson tried out a new maid, a girl named Sally Hawkins, while you were away?'

'Yes,' said Holmes, 'but I don't see—' and

then the detective fell silent. I winced. He grasped my shoulders and spun me around to face him. 'But that was before the King of Bohemia approached me for the first time. What could you possibly have meant by it?'

'I knew that he was planning to come to you, and I decided to strike first in case some sort of bargain was necessary. Mrs Hudson hardly took her eyes off me, but I found five minutes to look through your small collection of photographs. Your disorganisation was beneficial to you, or else I'd have come away with much more. As it was, I only had time to conceal one very old photo of you and the man I now know to be your brother, though I did not realise it at the time. I hoped I had been lucky—that if I ever needed the photo as a bargaining tool, it might be worth at least something small to you. I would have tried again, but Mrs Hudson very wisely did not trust me and put me out of the house.' Holmes listened to this speech impassively, and I had no idea what sort of thoughts might be going through his mind.

'Listen, Holmes,' I finally said, 'at the time, I did not know you, and I felt the need to arm myself against the most skilled detective in London.'

'And, I've no doubt you would do the same today, if you felt the need,' he said drily, looking down at me with a half smile.

'Yes, that's probably true,' I replied without

flinching, 'but I'm sorry it's become a player in whatever it is we're trying to investigate. I kept it with my papers, stored at my bank in London. Barnett must have helped himself to it and probably to everything else as well, whatever your brother's people were unable to access.'

'Well, at any rate, we still don't know for sure whose likeness he was after, whether my brother's or my own.' He patted my shoulder awkwardly. 'I'd have done the same if I were you.' From him, the compliment was a high one.

'Well, it appears my news is less than cataclysmic,' I said, sitting on the edge of the bed. 'We had one customer, a world-weary woman who was eager to share her unhappiness with Sanchez's operation with anyone willing to listen. It seems he lured workers from other growers with the promise of higher pay, but now seems to be driving them like Pharoah and the Hebrew slaves.'

'So I gathered,' Holmes said, taking his place in the chair opposite me. 'I'm glad to hear the comparison, since I did not know if the conditions I witnessed were typical or not. One wonders how long the men will endure the unpleasantness. Certainly, Sanchez could hardly hope for more than two more weeks from them under such conditions.'

'I assume they're in something of a bind,' I said. 'Would the other growers be likely to take them back this late?'

'Doubtful,' said Holmes. 'Whatever his part in your matter, this Sanchez seems an unpleasant character. Of course, the pertinent question is why he's so eager to get his harvest in before anyone else.'

Holmes opened his notebook. 'Let us evaluate our position.'

'First, we now know that a photo of Mycroft and me has changed hands, leading to recognition. The specific nature of the connection between Barnett and Sanchez remains unknown, but is confirmed, at least, by that. The presence of the photo on the desk confirms that Sanchez considers it important, at any rate.

'Second, we know that Sanchez not only intends to bring in the harvest, but to do so two weeks before his rivals. There is no market value to this; demand is steady. His motive must be completion itself, but why? That is suggestive, I believe, of the fact that whatever part of the plot is to take place on his end will be completed within a fortnight.

'Third, we know that Barnett has tampered with your private papers. We can safely assume that he has been notified by now that his prized songbird has flown the coop, but he should not know where, at least not yet.

'Fourth, we know that Sanchez was not unwilling to mention my presence to someone else, dismissing it as harmless. This suggests that he either does not think I am on his trail, or he is trying to double bluff by appearing not to care. This also assumes Ambrose McGregor is entirely truthful, which seems likely, but is not certain.

'Fifth, there remains no indication that Sanchez is aware of your presence or appearance. That suggests Barnett intended to conduct the Adler side of the affair himself.'

'But Holmes, why would Barnett think it necessary for his associate to receive a photograph if he was doing the work on the English side?'

'It could be a precautionary measure, but it's more likely that he expected either Mycroft or me to turn up here.' Holmes shook his head. 'I begin to think my movements were somehow anticipated.'

'Do you think I betrayed you?' I asked the question point-blank, which seemed to me the most logical course of action.

'The thought has crossed my mind,' he answered, not unpleasantly.

'Mine too,' I said, 'I mean, it has crossed my mind that if I were part of the plot, then some of the things we've learned would make much more sense.' Holmes let out a dry laugh.

'That would make me the object, rather than yourself,' he said.

'That can't possibly—' I stopped. 'There's something else I haven't told you.'

Chapter 8: Holmes

Holmes watched Irene dig her fingernails into her palms. 'Three months after I was married, Barnett contacted me. He came to our house in Yorkshire and requested, as my former solicitor, to see me. My husband was angry, but he didn't want to make a bad impression on a prominent fellow solicitor, so he allowed the meeting. Barnett's reason for coming was to make an offer to help me out of my marriage. He said he could prove Godfrey was an unfit husband and extricate my money if I would only do as he asked. I was suspicious, but I knew that he had connections in the law and on the bench. Obviously, I declined his offer.

'All he asked was for one favour, one job and he would take care of all of it for me.' She paused for a moment and smiled at Holmes. 'I was told to break into a flat in a dull part of London, the part of London where no one fashionable lives and nothing happens. Once inside, I was to take a particular case and bring it to Barnett's office. This flat and case, he said, belonged to a very bad man, a man who deserved to be thwarted. I asked him the man's name, and he told me: Mycroft Holmes, the brother of the famed detective.'

For once, Holmes listened with his eyes wide open and his body alert. Irene continued,

'Barnett was aware of the role you played in my marriage and the events surrounding it, but he did not know that our skirmish had convinced me that you were an honourable man or that I considered us fully even and had no desire to continue our little war. You may not believe that I also objected to the idea of petty thievery against someone about whom I knew nothing except his connection to someone I respected. At any rate, Barnett did not seem angry, but he refused to help me if I did not do as he wished. At that point, I owed him nothing, as all my funds were my husband's.

'You will no doubt be wondering now why I appealed to such a man after my husband's death. I am not entirely sure myself, as I can't imagine my doing so under normal circumstances. At the time, however, I was nearly paralysed with fear. I was terrified that the law would somehow contrive a way to keep me bound, to keep my fortune in the estate and leave me penniless. I believed that Barnett could prevent this, and I had never found him dishonest in his dealings with me, but I was surprised when he agreed to look after my property without anything in return except a small fee. I had expected some sort of request like the previous one. I should have known that he had found another way to use me.'

Holmes found himself resisting the urge to let his mind travel through the murky hallways of psychological theorising. 'You believe he is attempting to use you to get to Mycroft, then,' he finally said.

'Yes,' she answered decidedly. 'I believe it to be the only scenario that fits all the facts. Unfortunately, I have no idea how the man Sanchez fits into it.'

'Nor I, yet,' answered the detective, 'though your disclosures point to the original letter reaching my brother by design.'

'You have not asked me the reason for my reticence,' said The Woman after a pause. 'Does that indicate that you doubt my veracity?'

'Not in the least,' answered Holmes, beginning to fill his pipe with inferior tobacco from the shop. 'You and I have limited trust in one another. With knowledge of this condition, you chose to withhold information that had the potential to make you appear to be a possible criminal accessory in the current case.' He paused to close his eyes and take a drag from his pipe. 'More importantly, you're telling the truth now.'

Irene folded her arms. 'I hoped you'd at least doubt it for a moment,' she said, sounding disappointed. The detective opened one eye.

'You have tells, like anyone else, Miss Adler. If you haven't figured them out yourself, I'm certainly not going to enlighten you.' Irene let out an unintelligible sound that resembled a *hrff*. 'Your solicitor is not a stupid man. He may have misjudged Mycroft's likelihood of involving himself personally, but he did not mistake his willingness to act on information that pointed to criminal activity.'

'But what could Barnett have against your brother?' asked Irene curiously. 'He's certainly not visible or famous. You said he was some sort of diplomat.'

At this, Holmes laughed silently for some time. 'That, Irene, is perhaps the easiest thing of all. My brother is entirely unknown and unseen, except by those who have cause to despise him. He is an important man; even I do not understand the full extent of all he knows.'

'Is he a bad man, then?' The question was innocent, almost like that of a child, but the tone was ironic.

'Only to those who consider power wielded in the service of order to be an evil.'

Irene placed a delicate hand over her mouth and yawned. 'What do you intend to do now?'

'Tomorrow, we will deliver supplies to Sanchez's field office, and I very much hope the man himself will be in evidence.'

*　　　*　　　*

For the first time in a good while, Holmes's mind had enough to consider to keep it fully active through the night, mulling over the facts that had come to light through the day and evening. Ever since the concert, he'd suspected Irene of hiding information, and he wished devoutly that she had revealed what she knew earlier; nevertheless, he didn't blame her for her reticence. She'd been through a great deal, and her still-frayed edges proved that her experiences continued to eat at her psyche. No sense lamenting what couldn't be. The case was beginning to take shape as a simple plot of misdirection, a red herring by the name of Irene Adler, put out to somehow entrap Mycroft Holmes. Mycroft was an audacious target, but Holmes realised that his own presence in Florida was proof that the plot had not been entirely ill-conceived. If he had indeed been dead, would Mycroft have come himself? The detective doubted it, vehemently. Mycroft would have sent an associate to protect Irene, whether she liked it or not, as was his usual practice. Holmes wondered why such otherwise thorough plotters had been so sure his brother would do what his brother had never in his life been likely to do. There must be something, he thought, that he was missing. Now that Sanchez knew he was alive, had the plan changed? Surely, Barnett would be only too eager to use him to get at his brother. Was Sanchez trying to find him? If so, he was doing a fairly incompetent job. And why hadn't he made any effort when he had a chance at the Edisons' party? Holmes had many questions, but they were focused questions. He preferred those to vague certainties.

*　　　*　　　*

The citrus grove was pleasant in the early morning. A breeze blew the leaves of hundreds of trees, and Holmes enjoyed the pleasantly overpowering aroma of the fruit. The workers were not yet tired from the day, and the serene organisation of the harvest gave no hint of the owner's dark purposes.

Holmes led Irene around row on row of trees to the small shack on the far side of the grove. No one accosted them along the way, and he surmised that the foremen knew he was expected. 'I wasn't anticipating the smell,' said The Woman.

'Indeed,' said Holmes. Tom Perkins was a taciturn fellow. His 'wife' carried a bag of cigarettes in one hand and held his arm with the other, while he hoisted a box of canned soup on his shoulder. Together, they formed a less-than-savoury picture, he with his sagging eyes and florid face, and his wife with unkempt hair and soiled dress.

Holmes pushed open the door of the office, and Bill, the tall, broad grove supervisor greeted him with a less-than-enthusiastic *eh*. 'Good morning,' said the detective, his voice ingratiating. 'My wife and I have brought the items you requested.' Bill ushered them into the tiny building, pointing to a dusty room covered with piles of non-perishable goods.

'We've no mind to leave these until we've agreed on a price,' said Irene shrilly, holding tightly to her tobacco and nodding to a dull-acting Holmes not to relinquish his cans.

'I told you yesterday,' said Bill, glowering at Holmes and ignoring Irene, 'that I can't set a price until I've asked the Boss.'

'Well, then, I guess we'll have to take these things back to town,' said Irene, staring boldly at the foreman and hugging her sack like a prized turkey.

'Aye,' said Holmes after a pause. Bill stared at the couple for a long moment in which he seemed to be contemplating inflicting bodily harm before stomping into a room at the back of the shed and leaving them alone. Holmes winked at Irene.

After a moment, two voices could be heard, one Bill's angry growl, the other quieter and calmer. Bill's irate complaints were easy to understand, but Holmes couldn't make out the contributions of the other man until the door opened and both emerged.

The second man was considerably shorter than the foreman, dark-skinned and dark-haired, with a well-kept moustache and immaculate clothing. He smiled at Holmes and Irene, showing rows of perfect teeth that somehow put the detective in mind of a self-satisfied shark.

'Sir, Madam, what may I do to assist you?' The man's English was perfect, too perfect for a native, too well enunciated. He touched his chin and contemplated the pair placidly.

'Look, Mister, do you want our things or not?' Irene stepped forward defiantly

'My associate (he indicated Bill with a nod) informs me of your offer. I hope this will be sufficient.' He reached into his jacket pocket and pulled out a roll of bills, peeling two off the top and handing them to Irene, who eyed them greedily before surrendering them to Holmes, who glowered at her wordlessly.

'That's . . . satisfactory,' said Irene, attempting to look as if she were excited and trying not to appear so.

'Aye,' said Holmes.

'Come back next week with more of the same,' said the Central American, smiling and throwing out his arm theatrically. 'I'm Sanchez, the owner.' Irene nodded sycophantically and took Holmes' s arm. The unprepossessing couple left the shack with many thanks from the animated boss and glares from his second-in-command.

The detective led Irene away from the grove, as silently as befitted his character, until they had reached the wagon and he had unceremoniously dumped her into it, like an unprized sack of potatoes. 'I thought you might have made a hole in my arm,' Holmes finally ventured, once the scrawny rented horse had begun the trek back to town and carried them a safe distance from prying eyes. 'You held on so tightly a crowbar couldn't have dislodged you. I'm not entirely sure Jane Perkins is quite so enamored of her lord and master as to make that necessary.' He half-smiled drily.

When Irene failed to answer after many moments, Holmes looked over at her and found her pale under her makeup, her eyes fixed straight ahead and hands clasped tightly together. 'Holmes,' she said, 'Alberto Sanchez is James Barnett.'

Holmes let the horse drive itself for a moment, blinking rapidly and staring at his companion. For a moment, he wondered if she was foisting some kind of ill-advised joke on him, but her face was far from amused. 'You are absolutely sure of this?' He drove again, and his brain began to work.

'Without doubt,' answered The Woman, sounding steadier. 'When he first came out of his office, I noticed something familiar about him—something about the way he walked, but it was that gesture, when he touched his chin, that let me know for sure. After that, I couldn't stop seeing it—in the shape of his head, his eyes, the way he smiled. I would swear it in court.'

'Watson would love this,' Holmes muttered.
'Eh?'
'Just like something out of one of his stories,

no embellishment needed.' The detective felt somehow that a plot twist so outlandishly dramatic was a personal insult, a thumbing of the nose at the rationality he tried to project. Ridiculously irritating.

An unexpected sound interrupted his reverie. Laughter, unfettered. In spite of her fear, Irene's face was filled with amusement. 'Well,' she said, putting her hand over her mouth, 'we will have to tell him all about it one day.' Holmes thought so, too, but he didn't answer.

Chapter 9: Irene

I found the sight of our dingy shop oddly comforting after the harrowing events of the morning. Holmes didn't know how close to collapse I'd been, how much it had taken for me to play my part in front of Barnett, wondering if he would recognise me from the same sorts of clues that had unmasked him in my eyes. We had been like a cat and a mouse, but I wasn't sure who was feline and who prey. I felt thankful, for once, for the playacting I'd had to do as Godfrey Norton's wife, the months and years of acting in front of the world as if all was well when I wanted to scream in protest. I had learned to scream on the inside, and that was exactly what I had done when James Barnett's cold eyes had looked into mine. I had screamed in my mind, but I had seen no recognition in his. Holmes's disguises had, seemingly, been effective.

My companion held out his hand and helped me out of the wagon gently enough to make up for Tom Perkins's earlier handling of his wife. Neither of us spoke until we were back inside the shop, seated behind the scarred front counter where we could see anyone who approached. The gun Holmes had kept hidden underneath his bulky clothing during the morning's visit was now lying on a shelf just behind us, where he could grasp it at a moment's notice.

'Sanchez and Barnett are one and the same.' Hearing Holmes state the truth somehow made it even more vivid. Only with effort could I even recall the original purpose of the morning's visit, to meet Sanchez and ascertain what sort of purpose he might have for the unholy speed of his operations. Now there was only the realisation that one man existed where two were expected and that two plotters were actually one.

'Is it possible, Holmes, that there was a real Sanchez at some point?' I asked after a while, feeling slightly dazed.

'Unlikely,' he answered. 'Consider the facts. Barnett would have had to take his place before his arrival in Florida. A switch any time after that would have been far too risky. Even the best artists of disguise would have trouble convincingly replacing, overnight, a man who has been seen by many people and has worked closely with at least one. Therefore, he would have had to get to Sanchez some time between Central America and Florida, a risky and complicated operation, not to mention an expensive one. Why not invent some other fake persona and insert himself into Floridian society some other way, if here he must be? No, I believe Sanchez is a wholly fake persona.'

I nodded. 'How does this affect your view of the ultimate object of the case?'

Holmes shook his head. 'I confess that I am somewhat at a loss to understand the man's motivation. He would hardly have created such an elaborate ruse for the sake of making even several thousand dollars from a citrus grove. At the same time, we know that he took the trouble of delivering into my brother's hands a letter indicating a plot against you. He fully intended Mycroft, at least, to believe that he was two different people. Of course, the original purpose for this move had to be to focus attention here rather than on James Barnett, solicitor. He correctly assumed that Mycroft would let Barnett lie for the time being in order to avoid raising suspicion, while he tried to sort out the plot from this end. During that small window of inattention, James Barnett slipped quietly away and took on his alternate character. He probably also preserved the appearance of his presence in London—having his paper brought in, his office lights turned on and off, his radio used, perhaps even going so far as to hire a stand-in. My brother, brilliant but not infallible, almost certainly assumed that Barnett was needed in England to keep his side of the scheme, your supposed side, going, so he did not anticipate such a thing, as I did not. In addition, his operatives would have been instructed to keep a certain amount of distance in order not to alarm Barnett, and that probably also helped to make the ruse successful.'

After Holmes had ceased speaking, I took the leather pouch that lay on the shelf beside his gun and opened it. I filled the small pipe carefully, wondering if he would be bothered by my solicitousness, and struck a match, watching its flame whisper a tiny light against the sunshine streaming in from outside. Holmes took the pipe without comment and began to smoke. Neither of us spoke for a long time.

'Your performance today was remarkable,' the detective finally murmured, his eyes closed. I stared at him in surprise, having supposed my part in the morning's proceedings to have been taken by him as a matter of course. 'I had known you to be resourceful, but your level of bravery I had not realised.'

'Not at all,' I answered. 'It would have been

a crime for him to cheat us out of fair pay for our wares.' Holmes let out a dry chuckle.

'What do you intend to do after this matter is concluded?'

I watched Holmes smoke and contemplated my future for the first time since I had joined him 'Singing is a life, but I still desire what I wanted when I married—quiet and peace. I have belonged to the world, and I would like to recede in it.'

Holmes nodded. 'I understand the sentiment, but people like you and me are ill-equipped for ordinary lives, it seems.'

'One may be extraordinary in solitude.'

'In theory, yes, but not in practice.'

'You have certainly lived your belief.'

'But you have not lived yours.'

'Not yet, Holmes. I'm not in the grave.'

'No, certainly not.' He smiled, and we lapsed into silence again. I mulled over the details of the case, trying to apply Holmes's own reasoning methods, but I found myself circling back to the same details over and over, unable to think beyond the obvious.

'I admit,' I said finally, turning to him, 'that I am at a loss.'

'Are you?' The question was nonjudgemental in tone. 'I wonder if you trust me enough to carry out a few plans that may seem nonsensical, but will, if I am correct, prove invaluable.'

'Why not explain yourself, then?'

Holmes set his now-cold pipe down in front of him and turned to me. 'I must trust you in this as much as you will have to trust me. We will separate, and you will have as many opportunities to double-cross me as I will have to do the same to you. I am willing to take the chance for the sake of the case. I believe that purposeful ignorance on your part will make your tasks much easier and put you in less danger if anything should go wrong.'

'Very gallant of you,' I said, in a tone that said the opposite.

'Not noble,' he replied seriously, 'but necessary.' I looked into the detective's face and studied it for a long time. We had been in a position of some trust for several days, but I had not felt particularly vulnerable. I had beaten the man once, and I believed myself capable of doing so again. This was different; this required me to put my concerns aside and believe that he had my interests in mind. It required me to act like a client.

'Fine,' I said, none too gracefully.

'It's almost a pity,' replied my companion. 'You do Jane Perkins terribly well.'

'Likewise,' I said, arching an eyebrow. 'I find Tom Perkins's silence remarkably refreshing.'

Holmes motioned me upstairs imperiously. 'Disappear Jane Perkins and reappear Lavinia James,' but my mind belonged to Irene Adler, and, truth be told, I enjoyed Holmes's dramatic streak immensely.

I found it a strange process to feel Jane's creases and blemishes melt away from my face and Irene reemerge to share her visage once again with the demure Lavinia. With relief, I traded the tattered and stained cotton dress of the morning for one of my own, a conservative brown frock that I usually wore to travel—nothing special, but fully respectable. Finally, I rearranged my hair, laughing to myself at the intentional mess Holmes had made of it. Before I left the room, I couldn't resist dabbing a small amount of the detective's rouge on my pale cheeks. A respectable woman like Lavinia James wouldn't have dreamed of painting her face, but I had no such reservations, and the colour appeared natural. I amused myself imagining how horrified a real Lavinia would be at the amount of paint I normally wore when I performed.

'You'll have to wash your face again,' Holmes announced unceremoniously when I again joined him downstairs. 'You look painted.' I did as he said with the utmost annoyance. He shook his head again when I tried to return to my place behind the store counter. 'Lavinia James remains on the other side,' he said. 'As we currently appear, if we are seen to be familiar, suspicion will be immediately aroused no matter who our observer is.'

'Fair enough,' I said, taking up a can

of beans with mock seriousness. 'Are we permitted food, or is that forbidden during this phase of the investigation?'

'Not at all,' Holmes answered. 'Feel free to eat any of the wares; just take care to do so out of view of the road.' I ducked behind a barrel to absorb my meal.

Five minutes later, a customer walked through the doorway of Sloane's General Store. As quickly as I could, I slipped into the furthest recess of the room, a back corner behind tall wooden shelves, trying not to think about what sorts of creatures might have chosen to share such a hiding place.

The customer was a young woman whose white lace dress obviously belonged to someone far too well-heeled for this section of Fort Myers. She turned her face toward Holmes and smiled in response to his abrupt greeting, and I saw who she was: Marion Edison. True to form, Holmes didn't even flinch. 'Need anything particular?' asked the American accent of Tom Perkins.

'Nothing,' she answered, a little too brightly. 'I'll just look around.' I didn't move a muscle, hoping she wouldn't venture beyond the shelves near the front of the store. Thankfully, she left within ten minutes, thanking Holmes in a forcedly cheerful voice before she stepped into the street. Once she had gone, Holmes waited a few moments and quietly followed her out. I didn't dare to show myself until he returned several minutes later.

'All clear,' he said after he'd shut the door behind him. I emerged and dusted myself off, looking at him curiously.

'I assume you followed her,' I said. 'Did you discover anything pertinent? Her behaviour was certainly unusual.'

'Nothing apparent. She went to the restaurant at the end of the street and was met by a German army officer who was out of uniform. I gather she came here to avoid being seen in the street while waiting for her appointment.' I didn't ask how Holmes had divined that the man was a German officer. No doubt, he'd have had a long list of details that yielded the information.

'I wonder if her father knows of the connection.'

'Hardly our concern,' said Holmes, and I had to agree, though I couldn't help wondering.

'Now,' I said, 'tell me what you wish me to do in this guise.' I walked to the counter and stood in front of him, my arms folded.

'It's simple,' he said calmly, 'I wish you to reenter society with the story that your husband Bernard has returned to England on business, but that you have remained behind to look after his interests here. You will go to the Keystone Hotel on Park Street and use the money on your person (I had no idea how he knew about that) to procure a room in the name of Lavinia James. You will send notes to the Edisons and McGregors, informing them of your presence and apologising for your earlier disappearance. You will wait for invitations. If pressed by Ambrose McGregor, you will tell him that you are married to the detective Sherlock Holmes and that a case has called him back to England. The lovely and charming Lavinia James will not be left on her own for long, I'm sure.'

'How do you wish me to communicate with you?' I asked the question as soon he was quiet.

'I will communicate with you if necessary. Do not come here or try to contact me.'

I stared the detective down as hard as I could. 'Holmes, are you trying to get rid of me while you work?'

He looked straight back, equally resolute. 'I have already told you this is necessary. Believe me or not as you will.'

'Fine,' I practically spat. 'What information am I to seek?'

'I want you,' he leaned toward me slightly, 'to make it appear that you have never existed in the world as anyone except Lavinia James and to make her as socially visible as possible. Can you do that?'

'I will do it,' I said, 'but if it turns out to be without purpose, you won't get away easily.'

'Don't worry, Madam,' he answered coolly, 'I wouldn't dream of putting the great Irene

Adler to any extra labour. That would cost extra.'

'Holmes,' I said suddenly, my tone serious, 'Sanchez is part of the Edisons' social circle. How do I keep from being recognised without a disguise?'

'Leave his whereabouts to me,' said the detective. 'All the while you're working, I'll be just as busy. You will be safe.'

'Working,' I mumbled, going upstairs to gather my things, 'more like being put out of the way.'

Chapter 10: Holmes

Holmes was worried. He watched The Woman disappear toward the better-kept part of Fort Myers, and he couldn't help feeling concerned that things wouldn't proceed according to plan. He hated the necessity of separation. If Irene had been Watson, he wouldn't have been so concerned. Watson was used to the procedure and used to the risks. He was also meticulous about following orders and not overly curious about their meanings. But Irene Adler was none of those things. The one thing that comforted him was her frankness. He did not believe she'd have agreed to the plan disingenuously. Far more like her to take a stand and refuse to move than to stab him in the back after agreeing. Still, it was a risk, and he disliked risks when they concerned someone other than himself. The detective forced his mind to stop musing on possibilities and went upstairs to ready himself for his next task.

This time, he dressed as a day labourer but did not change his face. The speed with which he affected the transformation in his clothing made him wish his final objective could be accomplished with the same ease.

Holmes left a badly-written note on the shop door and walked to the grove in the afternoon. It was a walk of several miles, but he wanted to be unencumbered by horse or wagon. He skirted the perimeter of the grounds, moving around the rows of trees to the place where the office stood, approaching it from behind. He hid to the side of the structure, in the middle of a morass of the wooden crates the harvesters used to store picked fruit, crouching down and looking through a gap in the wooden slats. He waited, listening for any suggestion that the office might be occupied. As his ears adjusted, he caught the clicks of a typewriter and low voices. Thankfully, none of the outdoor labourers came near the building or the pile of boxes, but no one emerged from the office, either. Holmes was used to long periods of waiting; he had trained his mind to remain concentrated on the task at hand, but also to go elsewhere and reason through the facts of the case. His body rested, but it was poised to retreat or repel attack at a moment's notice.

The sun signaled late afternoon before he detected any movement. The voices he'd heard intermittently came nearer the door, and a young woman emerged, the source of the typing noises he'd heard earlier. He noted from her clothing and hands that she was a secretary, likely only required on occasion, since she hadn't been in evidence during his previous visits. She walked by Holmes's lair without looking at it. Typical, he thought. People saw things but didn't notice them.

Holmes heard the bang of doors opening and closing and things being moved about before the large figure of Bill the foreman finally left the office. He was more vigilant than his predecessor, as if he was worried that unhappy employees might be lurking in the shadows to accost him. He glanced toward the pile of wooden crates, but didn't appear to see anything amiss and moved on, whistling as he moved further away from the shed.

The building and the area around it were finally silent to Holmes's ears, but he did not move for some time before creeping out of his hiding place and moving slowly around the shack, staying low to the ground and stopping to take cover behind trees and detritus every few feet. He supposed the shed to be empty now, but he had ascertained, from his knowledge of its layout, that he would not be able to hear anything emanating from Sanchez's personal office unless he was on the other side of the building, which presented very little opportunity for cover. Holmes waited until the half light of dusk before skulking well under window height across the back of the structure and to the corner where Barnett's alter-ego conducted his business. The only cover available was a spindly sapling, but Holmes took his chance, knowing that darkness would soon hide him completely. He listened, but no sounds emanated from the dark building, and he began to feel more certain about its emptiness. No one emerged into the growing darkness for another half hour, and when daylight had finally disappeared completely, Holmes waited for his eyes to adjust and then crept to the wall that enclosed the windowless back office. Still no sound.

Confident, the detective quietly made his way to the front door. The flimsy building had no lock on its outside, so he easy pushed it open and slowly made his way inside, his right hand on the gun tucked into his waistband. He moved through the empty building warily, his eyes darting around for any sign of movement, but there was none. Finally, he reached the door of Sanchez's office, which was locked. The *great man* required more security than his associates, then. Holmes took his picklocks from his pocket and made short work of the silly thing.

Sanchez's field office was tiny and bare, containing only two chairs and a large desk with a few papers on its wooden surface. Holmes looked through them carefully, making sure to return them to their exact positions, but he found nothing beyond sales receipts and tally sheets that related to the grove's output. No matter. He hadn't come to find things out. The real information would be at the main office in town. He turned to go, taking a rolled-up handkerchief out of his left pocket and laying it haphazardly on the desk. The blue 'IN' on the corner stood out from the white of the cloth like a calling card.

Holmes made his way back to town in the darkness, folding his arms against the rare chill that had infused the Floridian night after the sun's departure. He was relieved that the first phase of his plan was complete, and his mind went to Irene. She was perfectly capable of putting her side of the plan into motion, but it was her willingness that concerned him. He wished he could simply call the Fort Myers police, whatever sort of operation that might be, and have Alberto Sanchez arrested for criminal activity; however, he had nothing of the man's to prove the connection except the letter, which was addressed to his name but did not indicate his level of involvement. Without more, who would believe the word of two strangers, two foreign strangers, no less, that Alberto Sanchez was actually a dishonest London solicitor? The idea seemed farfetched, even to Holmes, who knew that it was true.

Before the detective reentered the shop, he checked the lock for signs of tampering. He doubted anyone else would want to break into the place, but he had no trouble imagining Irene Adler doing so. Seeing nothing unusual, he went inside and walked around the room, looking for evidence that anyone had been inside. He found none, and upon ascending to the upper apartment and finding it similarly untouched, he became convinced that Irene had honoured her agreement and made no attempt to return, and, furthermore, that no one else had entered the premises. Relieved, Holmes readied himself for sleep. He had slept almost none for the past week, and he could feel himself running down. He hated the necessity of sleep, but he was not stupid enough to try to cheat the inevitable, and so, as he took his place in the chair by the window, he allowed his eyes to close.

When Holmes awoke, he ate absently, downing enough of his repugnant canned wares to keep him moving for the time being, and dressed himself in the expensive clothing of Bernard James. He did not, however, leave his face untouched, but altered his features to resemble a slightly older and less angular man. His walk as he left the shop was that of someone shorter than his six feet. Holmes had long before learned various ways to alter the appearance of what could not be changed. Most witnesses, questioned under oath, would have estimated his height as significantly below the reality when he chose to employ these methods aggressively. He would spend the day uncomfortable, but that was a small price to pay for relative anonymity.

Holmes followed the path Irene had trodden the previous day, moving quickly, like a man with an agenda to keep. He did not greet anyone in the street and gave the impression of someone who considered himself far above the section of town in which he found himself. When he moved into the more fashionable sector, he relaxed slightly and nodded to those he passed, making his way to a tall, imposing red brick structure. This part of town seemed more permanent, somehow, as if even the buildings of the rich were less transient than those frequented by the migrant workers who kept the city's economy moving.

Entering the building, Holmes saw an extremely young, smartly-dressed man at a desk. 'I understand this to be the office of Mr Alberto Sanchez,' he said, his voice clipped and impatient.

'Yes, Sir,' said the secretary, slightly abashed, 'but he's out.'

'Very well,' said the detective, feeling

fortunate. 'Will he be in today?'

'Yes, Sir,' the young man answered, taken aback at Holmes's harsh tone. 'He has appointments here all evening.' The secretary's eyes were wide. Holmes hadn't expected to be quite so fortunate as to learn his object's plan for the night; the boy's fear had been oddly helpful. The detective studied his face for a moment before determining that he wasn't lying.

'Give him this, please.' Holmes handed the young man a card, turned, and left the building before the recipient could realise that the object in his hand read 'Irene Norton.'

Holmes's next objective was the Keystone Hotel, a small establishment at the end of Park Street. Its small size and white-washed block exterior hardly suggested the grandeur of establishments in larger cities, but it was one of only two hotels offering rentable lodging in town beyond the odd room to let in places like Mrs Stillwell's. Still, as modest as it might appear, it catered to rich speculators and vacationers, the only people wealthy enough to afford its rooms. As a result, it was one of the few places in the city where Lavinia James would be expected to feel comfortable within her own class.

Holmes positioned himself at a table outside a café across the street and ordered coffee from a smiling girl who seemed delighted at the prospect of a tip at a time in the morning when most had finished breakfast and lunch was far away. With impatient bad temper, the detective requested a newspaper and opened it to shield his face. The *Ft. Myers Press* was hardly a goldmine of journalistic scintillation, but he scanned it anyway, looking for inconsistencies and anomalies. Force of habit drew him to the classified advertisements, as the Americans called them. He read down the list: animals for sale, jobs needed, jobs open, and finally, just above the bottom of the paper:

Birds leave their nests and migrate south. M.

The meaning was obvious. How Mycroft had contrived to plant an advertisement in this particular paper, his brother had no idea, but he mentally scolded himself for not thinking of the likelihood before. He understood what the message indicated; Barnett had journeyed to Florida. He gathered that Mycroft did not yet know that Barnett and Sanchez shared a body in addition to a scheme.

Holmes waited through three cups of decent coffee. He watched an elderly couple leave the hotel and a young boy enter and leave again with a parcel, no doubt bound for the town's tiny post office. He scanned the area with his eyes, noting the lack of anyone who seemed to have a particular interest in the hotel beyond the usual. He had hoped he might see Irene leave, but his primary object was to reassure himself that no one was tailing her—or himself.

Satisfied, the detective settled his bill and set down the none-too-generous tip that his character of the day would deem appropriate. He stood to leave, but as he did so, Irene emerged from one of the side doors of the Keystone, dressed in an elaborate green frock, her expression one of wide-eyed innocence. The detective abruptly resumed his seat and watched her over his open newspaper, taking care to keep his face in shadow. He was gratified to note that she scanned the area carefully and obviously noticed the presence of a man at the café, though his newspaper and apparent lack of interest appeared to convince her that he was not a threat, and she continued down the street without alarm.

After a few moments, Holmes left his table and newspaper and set off, following the same path as The Woman. He could see her far ahead, walking with the decorously slow pace of a polite lady. He slowed his walk to match hers, trying to look interested in the insipid shop windows he passed. For the moment, he wished Fort Myers were a bigger town so that two people on the street wouldn't be so conspicuous a sight. He had a close call when Irene turned to look behind her, but he was able to duck into a tiny alley and escape her eye. Holmes approved of her watchfulness. He was glad to know she wouldn't be taken easily.

Irene's path terminated at the edge of the Caloosahatchee River, where the River Cottages Hotel stood, another establishment catering to wealthy visitors. Holmes watched her enter the large vestibule and then exit again, following a young girl who led her around the side of the massive brick building. When the two were safely out of sight, Holmes entered.

'I'm an associate of Ambrose McGregor,' he told a stout, middle-aged woman who sat behind a counter reading a novel. 'Please point me to his room.'

'He's a popular guest,' she said. 'If you wait for the girl to get back, she'll take you to him, same as she took the lady.'

'That's all right,' said Holmes, putting impatience in his voice. 'If you give me the number, I'll go there myself.'

'Fine,' said the woman. 'Number sixteen, that way.' She jerked her head to the right, and Holmes nodded curtly and left. Once outside, he went back in the direction from which he'd come. Thus far, Irene was doing exactly as he'd asked, and things were progressing in the direction he'd hoped. Variables were never welcome, but he felt somewhat confident that her side of things would proceed along expected lines—as long as she stuck to plan.

The detective's next stop was the tiny telegraph office that adjoined the post office, where a sleepy elderly man was hunched over an old machine. He grinned broadly when Holmes appeared, apparently delighted at the prospect of an actual customer with a message to send. The man turned out to be a surprisingly quick and able operator, fortunately for him, since it meant he escaped the ire of the impatient businessman Holmes portrayed. The detective sent a message that he hoped would reach Mycroft in good time.

Our mutual friends are one not two STOP *S* STOP

After sending his telegram, Holmes made the long walk back to Sloane's General Store and transformed himself back into Tom Perkins. He took his place behind the counter, waiting, watching the road, and thinking.

Chapter 11: Irene

I remained irritated at Holmes for the amount of time it took me to hail a cab, ride to the Keystone Hotel, and engage a room. Once I saw the accommodations, my annoyance evaporated almost miraculously. I hadn't realised, until I saw the comfortable bed with clean white sheets, the immaculate bureau, and modern plumbing, how much the accommodations at Mrs Stillwell's less-than-pristine boardinghouse and the apartment above Sloane's General Store had begun to wear on me. I was willing to endure a great deal to achieve a goal, but I certainly didn't glory in grime and dirt. Holmes didn't like filth any more than I did, but once on a case, his mind was solely taken up with his purpose. I, on the other hand, had plenty of room to think extraneous thoughts about the vermin that might be crawling on my person while I slept. I was glad for the relief of cleanliness.

I waited a few moments in order to give the impression of fragile travel weariness and then rang for stationery. Lavinia James had no calling cards, of course, but I would make do with notepaper supplied by the hotel. I wrote first to Mina Edison and then to Tootie McGregor, stressing my delicate feelings of embarrassment at the brief disappearance of myself and my husband and explaining my current position of loneliness in an unfamiliar city. When I'd finished, I almost believed my own pathos.

The hotel supplied a porter, a fast-moving boy by the name of Simon, who was only too pleased to run an errand for an exorbitant price up front and the promise of the same when he returned an answer. I sent him to Seminole Lodge with both letters, anticipating that Mina would make sure her friend received the one intended for her, wherever Tootie might be. I was willing to perform detective work of my own if this attempt failed, but I saw no reason to take the roundabout way when the direct one would most likely suffice.

As I waited, I rested on an old grey brocade divan by the window and tried to wrap my mind around Holmes's plan. I knew he would take care of Barnett—I trusted him enough to believe that he would not let me be endangered by recogntion, but I couldn't think of a good reason for Lavinia James's reemergence, and my lack of understanding irritated me. Did Holmes also have plans for the inventor and his associates? I wondered, and I mused, and I could not reach an answer.

Thankfully, Simon quickly returned with two notes in tow. The feminine compassion of Tootie and Mina had not failed me. In fact, Tootie invited me to call on her and Ambrose at their suite in the River Cottages Hotel the next day, and Mina offered her home for the following evening. Holmes would be pleased, I thought, if he knew.

The rest of the afternoon and evening, I did something I had not done for some time—I read a novel, taken from the recesses of my trunk. It was about a lost soldier, a young detective, a flat, a German word scraped on a wall, and the colour red. I thought of Holmes, and I thought of Dr Watson and what I knew of them, and I smiled to myself. Most people thought the Holmes of reality was somehow less than the one they read about—less sharp, less brilliant, less exacting. The few who knew him well realised that he was actually more.

I slept well, and the morning found me ready to continue my half of the investigation, not that I understood what it was I was actually meant to be accomplishing. With a clear, rested mind, I could almost imagine that Holmes had good reasons for what he'd asked me to do, reasons beyond ridding himself of my presence.

I dressed in dainty green ruffles, all the better to appear as a timid and bereft wife for my visit, and ordered a vast breakfast. I derived a small amount of satisfaction from the notion that wherever Holmes might be, he certainly wouldn't be as comfortable or eating as well as I was. Sacrificing one's self for a case is well and good, but there's nothing wrong with a little enjoyment, one fact of which Holmes seemed sadly ignorant. I considered, though, as I speared an egg yolk and watched the decadent liquid spread, that enjoyment is a most subjective thing.

I waited until midmorning before asking the porter the way to the River Cottages and setting out on my way. I considered a cab, but the weather was too fine, and I fancied a walk to the river. For the first time since I had agreed to help Holmes, I took the gun from my trunk and tucked it into my handbag, imagining Lavinia's horror at such a thing. Nevertheless, it made Irene Adler feel secure.

The sun was bright as I made my way outside and swept the area with my eyes. I noticed a businessman engrossed in a newspaper at a café across the street, but otherwise, the street was clear. As I walked, I checked for followers a few times, but found no one. Still, I kept my hand on my bag, ready to retrieve my weapon if needed. I couldn't entirely shake the nagging fear that Sanchez-Barnett—had recognised me as his client during our previous interaction.

I reached the River Cottages in good time and was shown to the McGregors' vast suite, which overlooked the Caloosahatchee River. Tootie admitted me herself with a smothering embrace, though I noticed that she had a maid with her, a tall, middle-aged woman who looked as if she might be near-equal in determination to her employer. Ambrose stood up from a chair as I entered and greeted me gravely and politely. His eyes were curious and insistent, and I knew that I was not likely to escape an explanation. I considered trying to attach myself to his wife to avoid a private encounter, but considering how long Ambrose had lived with her, I didn't doubt he would have plenty of ways to get around her insistence. I decided to let things unfold as they would.

'My dear, you look positively famished,' said Tootie, as soon as I was seated on a plush chair 'Look at her, Ambrose. She's wasted away since we saw her.' I managed not to smile at the thought that it had been a mere few days since the Edisons' dinner. I was gratified at the thought that I looked slightly unwell. I had chosen the particular shade of green I was wearing because it made my fair complexion look even paler than usual All the better for Lavinia to appear frail. Tootie called for a meal, which turned out to be a somewhat appalling array of baked beets, fried artichokes, greasy beef, and canned pineapple. My long walk had made me slightly hungry, but I was relieved that the decorous Mrs James would never have been expected to eat very much at a time. I could pick at the fare without appearing impolite.

'Now,' said my hostess, spearing an overcooked beet with great force, 'tell us what happened to your Mr James. I sent a note to your boardinghouse and was told that the two of you had simply vanished. It was quite shocking, my dear! Quite shocking!'

'I apologise,' I said weakly, covering my face with my hand as if I were somewhere near tears. Tootie found a large yellow handkerchief somewhere on her person and handed it to me.

'I don't blame you, dear, but I'm terribly curious,' she continued. I thought quickly. I had considered a few different explanations I might use, but had ultimately decided to let the inspiration of the moment guide me.

'It was very surprising,' I began, which was true, since whatever I was about to say would certainly be a surprise to myself. 'The morning after we left the Edisons, we received a telegram that my husband's London partner had fallen ill, a man named Smith, who has been in business with him for many years. As a result, Bernard was needed right away so that the directorship of the English branch of the company would not be left vacant.' I said some of this as if I were slightly confused, the way a business-ignorant Lavinia might be.

'What sort of business is your husband in? I'm afraid I didn't catch it the other night,' Ambrose put in quietly. I resisted the impulse to react, wondering what he was trying to accomplish.

'Canning,' I said. 'He was hoping citrus might be a *helpful avenue of expansion*, as he likes to say. That's why I'm still here.' I turned to Tootie, smiling. 'He was so upset about his partner that he was ready for us both to go home, but he decided after thinking about it that I should remain here for the time being, in the hope that he will be able to return.'

'All by yourself!' Tootie shook her head, 'without even a companion! Well, don't worry. Mina and I will take good care of you. Even Marion seemed to like you, and she's usually difficult to impress.' I smiled thankfully.

'I'm ever so grateful, Mrs McGregor.'

'Don't worry, dear. That man is so delighted

124

with you that he won't be able to stay away. And who could blame him?' Holmes's face came into my mind, and I had to exert great effort to keep from laughing. The detective hadn't warned me of the odd moments during a case when something so strange or humourous happens that staying in character is an almost superhuman skill. Maybe he didn't find it so.

I spent another hour with the McGregors, admiring their river view and listening to Tootie's plans for them to purchase property and build a home of their own in town. Finally, she declared that I looked weary (after purposeful yawning and dullness on my part) and that I must rest until the evening's dinner engagement. She said that she would hire a cab, but I said that I would prefer the fresh air. I had not anticipated that Ambrose McGregor would insist on accompanying me, though I wasn't surprised. His wife beamed and sent me off with a kiss.

Once we had cleared the hotel grounds, Ambrose spoke. 'You're a very good liar, Mrs James—Holmes, I mean.' I fought the automatic urge to say *thank you*, as any polite American child is raised to reply when praised, but he hardly meant it as a compliment.

'First, Mr McGregor, I didn't intend to lie to you at dinner. I planned to meet with you and explain, but unforeseen complications beyond my control arose that required my husband

and me to disappear briefly.'

'Yes,' he said drily.

'As you said, my husband is not Bernard James, but Sherlock Holmes, the consulting detective. We came here to investigate a case that concerns interests both here and in England, but he was called back by developments there. I will remain here until he returns, learning whatever I can.'

'Are you investigating my family or anyone else who was present at the Edisons' that night?' The direct question was in keeping with the man's direct nature, and it did not shock me. I was relieved to be able to answer honestly.

'No, we are not. Our investigation concerns others. I wish I could tell you who they are, but I must keep my husband's confidence.' The last bit was half true. I wished I could trust him with the details of the case. At the same time, his very impression of solid respectability made me doubt him. Had he truly been the chance receiver of a comment by Sanchez about Holmes's identity, or did he play a larger part? I wished Holmes were with me, hearing and seeing what I encountered so that he could give his opinion. I disliked coincidences as much as he.

Ambrose nodded calmly. 'I suppose I have to accept that.' I felt sorry for the man I hoped he was. As we approached the entrance to the Keystone Hotel, he turned to me. 'I have not—

Mrs Holmes, I consider myself a gentleman, and it has never been my habit to importune respectable ladies. If you and your husband are on the side of right, then please accept my apologies.'

The only repayment I could give his kindness was my widest smile, but, without being ridiculous, I must admit that men usually seemed to find it a plentiful enough reward. He went on his way, and I returned to my room to make sense of things using the hotel's cheap stationery and my fountain pen to write down my thoughts.

Chapter 12: Holmes

Number 14 Charles Avenue. Holmes studied the rudimentary map of the city that the cheerful clerk of the town's one real general store had sold him just before closing. While he thought, he smoked a cheap cigarette in a repugnant alley where many others had obviously done the same, given the amount of refuse that littered the ground and the stale smell that lingered in the air. The map showed that he was in the right part of the city for the address he sought, and he didn't want to make his taxed feet walk all the way back to Sloane's to wait for dark. In the guise of Tom Perkins, he was below most people's notice, and he was able to move closer and closer to his object without attracting attention.

Finally, when the Florida night was covered in thick, humid darkness, he took the last steps to Charles Avenue, a street lined with opulent mansions, some of them even grander than the Edisons' home. He crept through a few well-kept lawns and skirted two that showed signs of having dogs somewhere on the premises. Number 14 wasn't vastly different from the others. It had the same appearance of new money, whitewash, and pride built into its wide porch and numerous windows. Holmes walked around it silently, ascertaining that the first floor was dark and silent while the second showed signs of occupants who were awake and active. All the better for his purposes. He stepped silently toward the front porch, hunching over to make himself as short as possible. When he reached it, he took a box of ladies' face powder out of his pocket and dropped it willy-nilly on the porch floor. Not waiting to see if the sound had roused anyone, he ran back to the road and didn't slacken his pace until he was far away.

Holmes again forced his weary feet to carry him to the Keystone Hotel. No one was around its outside, so he went to the door from which Irene had emerged during the day, a door into one of the large ground-floor suites. He listened, but he could hear nothing. It was too late for her to be at dinner, but he hadn't expected her to be asleep, either. He wanted to be unsuspicious, to trust that Barnett had conducted meetings in the guise of Sanchez all evening and taken no time for a society dinner party, but he couldn't silence the worry in his mind.

Concerned, Holmes went into the front entrance. A young porter, not more than fifteen at the oldest, sat behind the desk, playing cards. 'What do you want?' he asked, taking in the unpleasant visage and attire of Tom Perkins.

'Has Mrs James come in?' Holmes asked in an ingratiating tone.

'Why would I tell you that?' asked the lad, staring belligerently.

'Because of this,' Holmes spoke in his normal tone and produced a group of coins whose combined value was more than a porter would be likely to make in a week. The boy's eyes bulged.

'No harm, I guess,' he said, holding out his hand. 'She ain't come in anyhow.'

Holmes wished the boy were lying, but the detective could tell he was sincere. He handed him the coins. 'Now,' he said, still in his own voice, 'if you tell anyone else where the lady is, I'll know about it, and you won't get off so easily.' The boy looked nervous, but Holmes turned tail and left. Once outside, he ran.

The detective didn't know the last time he'd done so much legwork in one day, but he didn't care. He had one place in mind, and if that failed, his case would be about more than identity and theft; it would be about finding a missing woman. *Just until tomorrow* he thought angrily. Today was the day—the only day—the only time he'd had to leave things to move as they would. He hadn't believed the man would act so quickly. Mistakes—he'd made them before, but not often. Had he been incorrect now in thinking he had time?

Holmes's weary body finally carried him to Sloane's General Store. With sinking heart, he looked at the lock and found it intact. Cursing his own faith, he took out his key to open the door and give himself one last chance not to be entirely wrong. He nearly called out when the door opened of its own accord. The Woman stood on the other side, dressed in a purple gown. 'Good evening, Mr Holmes,' she said, opening it wide to admit him. His fear threatened to turn into wrath for a moment, but logic subsumed it. He had expected this, had known that no matter what he said, she was likely to return. Relief, too, had its place— larger, perhaps, than he had anticipated.

'I'm sorry,' were the next characteristically blunt words out of her mouth. 'I needed to talk to you, and I didn't know what else to do.' As she had done once before, she went behind the counter and retrieved the detective's pipe, filling and lighting it before handing it to him.

'I'm entirely unsurprised,' said Holmes after

a few drags of his pipe, forcing himself not to betray his previous worry. 'What is it you wish to tell me?' Irene sat on the edge of the counter, not seeming to care what impression her presence might give to outsiders, her dress strangely out of place among the grimy wares.

'I think Ambrose McGregor might be in league with Sanchez,' she said. 'I'm not sure his knowledge is as coincidental as we thought.'

'What did he say?' asked the detective calmly. Irene gave a detailed account of her meeting with the man, ending with a restatement of her questions about his possible motives.

'Let us consider,' said Holmes quietly. 'If he is part of the plot, why would he make a point of speaking to you? Furthermore, why would he emphasise that he knows me?'

'To try to discover your whereabouts for his accomplice?' Irene asked. Holmes opened his eyes and looked at The Woman.

'A fair question,' he said. 'I'll grant you that it's not entirely possible to rule him out. Still, if he had designs on you, he had a perfect opportunity to act on them.'

'That I grant you,' said Irene quickly, 'but if your brother—or even you yourself is the object, then his actions make more sense.'

Holmes did not tell her what he suspected. He still believed, even after the evening's worry, that she must not know, for fear that she would unwittingly do something to make the entire plan come crashing down.

'I take it,' he said after a while, 'that your dinner with the Edisons was uneventful, since you haven't mentioned it.'

'Very,' she said simply. 'It was only a family party with me and the McGregors as additions. Ambrose didn't say a word to me the whole evening.'

'I see,' said Holmes quietly. 'You may be interested to know that the case is progressing exactly as it should. Until this unexpected change of plan, you had played your part admirably.'

Irene looked over at him as if she'd like very much to hit him. 'How dare you?' she said, getting up and standing in front of the counter to face him. 'I know what your clients feel like now, how manipulated, like chess pieces. I don't know how they stand it.'

'My clients do as I wish because they trust the outcome,' Holmes said drily.

'Well, pity I know you're not infallible then,' she threw back, her eyes on fire. 'You give me no way to contact you, force me into a character that leaves me vulnerable to recognition, and now—you have the gall to complain that I've *deviated from plan*.'

Holmes wondered how he'd arrived here, to a point at which he had a partner who was intrinsic to the case but impossible at the same time. Watson trusted him, almost too much sometimes; he was brave, but his bravery was rarely creative. He served the plan, whatever it was. The clients, too, almost always followed whatever parts of the plan he gave them, out of desperation and trust. Even the police grudgingly came around to his way after a while. Lestrade had been proven wrong too many times.

The Woman was different. She had beaten him, and it made something different between them. She had seen his cracks, and she could not see him uncritically. Against the odds, she seemed to have mustered some sort of trust in him over the previous days, but that appeared to have evaporated in the midst of her worry over Ambrose McGregor.

Irene turned her back to the detective, her arms folded. 'Tell me why I can't know, Holmes,' she said from between clenched teeth. 'Make me believe you.'

'I can't,' he said simply. 'I have a plan, and I believe it will succeed. I can guarantee you my best efforts and my protection, but as you know too well, I cannot guarantee perfection. There was a time when I was very young that I thought myself invincible, but that was a long time ago. You must make your choice based on what you know of the man I am—based on logic.'

After a very long time, Irene turned slowly and faced him. 'I wish I didn't trust you,' she said, then turned and walked out of the store.

She didn't know that moments after she left, the bone-weary detective followed her. She didn't see him mirror her steps all the way to the Keystone Hotel, and she was ignorant of the vigil he kept while she slept.

This phase of the plan was new. The Woman had no idea that the day of separation was over, and now Sherlock Holmes was determined not to let Irene Adler out of his sight. He sat in an empty lot beside the hotel, his arms propped on his knees, his body finally at rest. No one was out so late at night in the fashionable part of town, and he had only insects for company. He welcomed the physical rest, but he had no desire for sleep. He was beyond that now and at the point in the case that made his blood rush and his body cease to desire food or sleep. All he craved was the end, the solution. Other things receded, even his conversation with Irene. He recognised the near-disaster her refusal to help him further would have caused, but he did not dwell on it. She had made the right decision, and now it was for the man, the villain of the piece, to make his move.

Holmes thought, for a moment, of Watson, of how much the doctor would have enjoyed the waiting and the hunt. John had always been a soldier, and he always would be. They'd have sat together under the stars, not speaking, both alert, and he'd have felt the confidence of having a brother-in-arms.

But The Woman was inside. Walls separated them, but not purpose. She had agreed, and Holmes had seen the resolve twisted inside her anger. She would play her part, and she would play it well. She was no brother, but she was enough.

Chapter 13: Irene

I hated everything about my room. I hated the heavy tan drapes, the ugly floral wallpaper, the insipid lace coverlet. Everything seemed different now. I lay down on the bed in my purple gown and closed my eyes, but my thoughts were far too tumultuous for sleep. The most infuriating thing was that I had made the right decision, and I knew it. For savage amusement, I tried to imagine stolid Dr Watson railing angrily at Holmes for the part he'd been told to play in a particular case, but I couldn't manage it. Watson trusted him too much.

And so did I, irritatingly. I trusted him the way I had once trusted Godfrey. That was different, though. I had trusted Godfrey without really knowing him, staking my claim on a personality and a reputation, but not on my own knowledge and experience with the man. My trust in Holmes was just the opposite sort. What name and reputation had failed to do, my experiences with him had accomplished. Now that I knew him, I could not fail to trust him. Once again, I had entrusted a part of myself to a man, and that was something I had promised myself never to do again. But it was the right decision, the inescapable right decision. I finally fell asleep with my mind going around and around in circles, berating me on one hand and soothing me on the other.

The next morning, I awoke at peace, as if I had crossed some sort of barrier. I was committed, but I wasn't stupid. I took my handgun from under my pillow and put it back into my bag. It would accompany me wherever I went.

A few minutes after I finished breakfast, Marion Edison came to call. I received her in the hotel's main sitting room, wondering, when I saw her pale face, what secrets she might have, particularly about the German she had met. I doubted they concerned Holmes and me, but I was unwilling to ignore any anomaly.

'Good morning, Mrs James,' Marion said a little shyly as she joined me.

'Please call me Lavinia,' I answered, smiling and holding out my hand. She took it, and I noticed that she was strong.

'Would you walk with me?' she asked after a moment.

'Of course,' I answered. 'I'm new in town. Perhaps you can show me what I should see.'

I couldn't remember the last time I'd taken a walk with another young woman, and I found it ironic that the case was what caused me to do so now.

For a long time, we talked about nothing in particular. She asked about London fashions and I about American ones, we laughed at a duck crossing the street, and finally we retraced our steps back to the café across from my hotel, thirsty and ready for a rest.

'I hope my husband is well,' I said as we sipped our tea.

'You must miss him,' said Marion quietly.

'I do,' I answered, 'very much.' I felt sorry for deceiving the girl so blatantly, but I hoped to draw her out by revealing personal feelings. Another part of my brain tried to remind me that if I had been a different kind of wife with a different kind of husband, I also might have felt those same feelings when I thought of Godfrey Norton, but I pushed it away.

'I—have someone to miss, too,' said Marion, hesitating.

'Oh?' I said noncommittally, thinking I might know something of what she was about to say.

'Last year, I took a trip to Europe with my aunt. The trip was difficult. I got smallpox, and the doctor thought I might even die.' She looked at me with the wide-eyed stare of a child who could not yet fathom the finality of her own death. 'But,' she continued, leaning forward with intense excitement, 'I met *him.*' I felt a surge of empathy. Some things are universal.

'His name is Karl Oeser, and he's a lieutenant in the German army.' I nodded and tried to look surprised. Marion lowered her voice, 'He's—come here, and I don't know how to tell my father and Mina. My aunt never knew how much we cared for each other.'

I tried to think of what Lavinia James would say to this, finally settling on, 'I'm afraid you'll have to tell them some time,' about which Lavinia and Irene could safely agree.

'I know,' said Marion, back to her usual directness. 'That's why I've told you first, to practise.' I smiled encouragingly, and she continued. 'I think he's going to ask me to marry him.'

'I hope you'll be very happy,' I said, and meant it.

I finished my tea, feeling a sense of satisfaction at having one mystery cleared up. As Holmes and I had both suspected, Marion's secret was a private one. It was a strange thing, I thought, to unravel someone's personal story in the midst of the danger and uncertainty of a case. There was something wrong about it, almost, as if people's personal lives should be spared the magnifying glass of detection, but it didn't work that way. As I knew from experience, private lives were often exactly where mysteries lay, and truth usually only emerged after invasive scrutiny.

Marion's enthusiastic thanks and impulsive kiss on my cheek as she left me at the entrance to the hotel reminded me that not everyone minded being found out. She was radiant in the knowledge that I knew her secret, and I couldn't help but hope that she would not regret her choice.

When I entered the Keystone once again, I was met by a porter with a note from Tootie McGregor, asking me to accompany her and her husband to the theatre that night. I was not excited at the prospect of meeting Ambrose again, but I could think of no way to refuse. I sent back my acceptance, glad that a theatre would, at least, provide little room for private encounters.

With the prospect of nothing to do until evening staring me down and no desire to put myself in needless danger by wandering around outside, I ran a bath in the gold-footed tub in my suite's opulent washroom and hung one of my finest dresses to be unwrinkled by the steam. I sat on the white tile floor while the tub filled, watching fog cover the mirror and wondering what Holmes was doing. My mind turned to Barnett, and I shuddered at the thought of the moment I'd realised he was standing in front of me as Alberto Sanchez. I hadn't known I could be brave enough to stay silent when I had so much fear. How often did Holmes feel afraid, I wondered, during the long nights and dangerous days? I realised then that I'd never thought of him as brave because he never showed his fear.

I luxuriated in the bathwater for ages. I had no idea how long I'd be Lavinia James, so I was determined to enjoy her luxury as long as I could. It was refreshing to be alone, with no maids and no husband, free from being Irene Adler, even. The case tugged at the back of my mind, but at the same time I felt curiously light, as if the bonds that had tied me down were finally loosening. My own decisions had gotten me where I was—no one forcing or pushing me, not even Holmes. As much as he his reticence had angered me, he had left my choices in my hands. There might be concealment between us—I could not forget that I had failed to tell him everything at first—but there was no underestimation or manipulation. We were equals in The Game.

As I stepped out of the water, I was determined. I put on my black silk gown and felt it glide over me like confidence. I would be Lavinia James tonight, demure and sweet, but underneath, Irene Adler would watch and wait, never knowing when the part I didn't understand would turn to something more, when the thin form and bright eyes of the detective would ask, and I would be swept away to become someone new. As I picked up my bag, the pistol in its depths felt natural, an important part of my ensemble.

The McGregors came for me in their carriage at half past six, and Ambrose helped me inside, his face blank. In contrast, his wife was an explosion of life in a red gown that accented the red in her cheeks and complemented her excitement. She eagerly seized my hand and declared her joy at the prospect of seeing *Hedda Gabler*, a reportedly shocking play by Henrick Ibsen, a Norwegian with extremely liberal views.

'My goodness,' she said, lowering her voice conspiratorially, 'I've heard the poor heroine shoots herself, right on stage! Mrs Warren does the part beautifully, they say.' I didn't tell her that I had seen many of Ibsen's plays and knew of this one, since I couldn't imagine that Lavinia James would care about such things. Ambrose sat across from us, staring at the floor. His wife seemed used to his taciturn ways and didn't mind filling up the space with her own words, for which I was grateful.

The theatre was one of the grander buildings in Fort Myers, a neoclassical edifice with columns, which served as town hall, meeting place for Freemasons and other civic clubs, and, as it would this night, a theatre for travelling companies. Society considered acting a less-than-respectable profession, but in Fort Myers, as everywhere, very few seemed to mind enjoying its product, and we were joined by many others as we entered the vaulted vestibule.

141

Tootie knew everyone and was quick to greet young and old and to introduce me as her friend. I gave out many a simplistic smile, all the while watching for Barnett, anyone else who looked as though they might recognise me as Irene Adler, and Ambrose McGregor, of whom I did not want to lose sight. Strangely, my different purposes made me calm rather than agitated, as if they formed the steps to my own mental dance of which I was leader. A step here, and I clasped the hand of a woman Tootie introduced as Mrs Johnson. A step there, and I ruled out a man with Sanchez's hair but someone else's face. A twist to the right, and I caught Ambrose McGregor in the corner of my eye, engaged in conversation with a man I didn't recognise.

Was this what Holmes felt, I wondered? The intense focus, the knowledge of one's purpose and task, the surge of adrenaline that came with danger, and the answering calm of total awareness—I knew them all, and I began to believe things might end well.

We finally took our seats in the fourth row, and I stared at the red plush curtain, thinking of the many times I had been on the other side, waiting to be revealed to audiences in countless theatres. I didn't know what I would do after the case was over and Holmes and I had parted, but I saw now with absolute clarity that I would never again sing to please a theatre crowd. Once, I had left singing to start a new life, but the tragedy of my marriage had caused me to seek solace in what I knew. After the case, I would need it no longer.

I leaned back in my seat and flicked my fan up and down in front of my face, welcoming the mental escape the play would bring. As the lights dimmed, anticipation washed over the audience like the tide coming in, and I could hear Tootie take a sharp breath beside me. Lavinia James watched the stage, to all appearances as excited as everyone else, but Irene Adler kept her hand on her bag, ready to produce her pistol at a moment's notice.

Chapter 14: Holmes

A tall, well-dressed man slipped into the theatre just before *Hedda Gabler* began. He allowed an usher to hurry him to a seat in the back row, but as soon as the man had gone, he got up quietly and slipped into a back corner. Sherlock Holmes stood in the darkness, his black suit blending into the shadows. This night, he firmly believed, was when the man would make his move.

For several moments, Holmes kept his eyes on The Woman's dark head. Her body was relaxed, but he could tell by the position of her arm that her hand was clutching something. Knowing Irene, he thought, it was most likely a weapon. He applauded her vigilance, but not the presence of a complication. With aversion, he realised he would have to rob her himself, provided Barnett gave him time. He was repulsed at the idea of betraying a partner, but the idea of a plan gone wrong was even more unthinkable.

Holmes enjoyed the first act. He appreciated Ibsen; the man was like a detective who had solved a case and then rewritten it with all the hidden motivations and human frailties on the surface instead of buried the way they usually were. Detection would be far easier, thought Holmes, if people behaved so transparently in real life. He ducked into a seat as the audience clapped for Act I and the lights rose.

A local tenor by the name of Steven Bartholomew shuffled to the stage to entertain in the interim, looking nervous. Holmes felt a surge of something surreal as the man's accompaniment began and he tentatively bleated out his first notes. The love song sounded nothing like it had in the mouth of Irene Adler, but Holmes's mind cast him back to the night when he had first seen her again, divine in violet, staring him down with every perfect note.

He made his mind return to the present, forcing himself to focus against distraction. A supposed plot against Miss A had brought him here, and he would not let himself lose concentration until the case was complete. Besides, Steven Bartholomew was one of the worst singers Holmes had ever heard.

Polite applause for the man's unfortunate effort heralded the dimming of the lights for Act II. Once again, the detective quietly slipped from his seat and took his place in the back corner of the auditorium, his eyes looking up and down each row to discern any changes. There were none. The same audience of well-to-do Floridians stared straight ahead, waiting to witness Hedda Gabler's ever-crumbling life played out in front of them.

As the second act drew to a close, Holmes waited for the intermission, his nerves taut. He sat again, waiting through a short speech by a member of the Fort Myers Salvation Army, then sprang to life as soon as the audience was dismissed.

Holmes's eyes found Irene in a few seconds, in the middle of a group of people pressing toward the door. He stayed well to the edge of the crowd, waiting for most of the theatregoers to move into the hall before he followed, but he did not allow Irene to pass out of his line of sight. Once in the vestibule, Holmes kept to the edges of the room and watched as Tootie purchased refreshments for herself, her husband, and her guest. He smiled to himself as Irene was plied with a drink that he could see she didn't want. Finally, Tootie shepherded her charge back toward the theatre, and Holmes prepared to make his move. The detective had made himself up to look slightly dissipated and beyond his own age, but he didn't want to risk Irene's notice through a direct confrontation. He would have to be quick.

Using the press of people to hide him, he made his way to a drink seller and purchased a glass of wine. Slowly, he moved closer and closer behind Irene, until only a few people separated him from The Woman and her companions. In a frantic split second, Holmes dropped the entirety of his wine on a large man in front of him, then ducked down in the midst of the confusion and extracted the pistol from Irene's handbag while she tried to calm Tootie, who was in danger of panicking. He couldn't tell if Irene had noticed the theft, but he knew she hadn't seen him. Even if she desired to report the loss, how would she explain her reasons for carrying a pistol? It wasn't the most elegant operation Holmes had ever carried out, but it had accomplished its purpose. He followed the crowd back inside the theatre and sat down, thankful for the dimming of the lights a moment later.

Holmes once again took his place in the shadows, but this time, he found the difference for which he had been watching. He counted the number of people in each row and found one extra in the last seat of the sixth, a man with dark hair—hair the colour

146

of Alberto Sanchez's dyed locks. Holmes's pulse quickened as he studied the man in the darkness, trying to be sure. If he didn't plan to move that night, Holmes thought, then he was a greater fool than the detective supposed. The end of Act III brought back the unfortunate tenor, and Holmes sat again, wishing the play would end. He couldn't imagine Barnett risking a panic in the theatre, so he doubted anything would happen before the final curtain. The last act was torture for the detective, his mind pushing forward to whatever might be coming. He watched Irene, surprised at the calmness in her demeanor in spite of the anxiety she must be feeling after the discovery of her loss. He had done what he knew to be necessary, but he despised the thought that he had caused her to be afraid. For a split second, he questioned himself and wondered if he should have disclosed the entirety of his intentions to her, but just as quickly he reminded himself that the plan depended on her not knowing. The fact that she might not agree once the operation was over had occurred to him, but it had no effect on his resolve.

Finally, the curtain closed after the suicide of the protagonist, and the stunned audience waited a few seconds before breaking into enthusiastic applause. As the lights rose and the cast members took their bows, the detective made his way to the entrance and waited unobtrusively until the attendees began to drift out, watching for horses and carriages to take them home.

Alberto Sanchez exited before the McGregors, and Holmes let him pass out of his line of vision and waited instead for Ambrose, Tootie and Irene, who were near the back of the departing crowd. Once again, he stayed at the edge of the press of people, watching and waiting, keeping pace with The Woman though physically separated from her. He had to be careful; Irene's watchful eyes were everywhere, and he could clearly see how ill-at-ease she was. To anyone else, she simply seemed agitated by the crowd, but he knew her thoughts were much darker.

Holmes was poised in the limbo of the moment, knowing that something was about to occur to change everything, but unsure exactly where or exactly how it would take place. He would have given a great deal to stop it before it began, but that would have broken the deal he'd made with himself. He wouldn't jeopardise the case because he was afraid for the lady, and he couldn't afford to put her in more danger later by eliminating the current peril. He felt as if his hands were tied, and she looked as if she anticipated the worst. He hated the increasingly desperate confusion he could see on her face. Irene Adler was meant to be strong. Irene Adler was meant to be brave. Irene Adler wasn't meant to look like a lost little girl.

Finally, the detective followed the thinning crowd outside. He stepped behind a white pillar and watched as Irene and her hosts stood on the steps of the hall and waited for their carriage. Irene stayed close to Tootie, as if she thought the older woman's presence might offer some protection.

The McGregors' carriage was one of the last to arrive, and Holmes watched as Ambrose helped his wife and The Woman inside before getting in himself. Was it possible, then, that he had misjudged Barnett's intentions? Suddenly, as the carriage left, he caught a glimpse of the driver's thick leather gloves. Bill the foreman had been wearing those gloves the night Holmes had seen him leave work.

The detective sprang into action, no longer caring if the remaining theatregoers saw him. He raced across the street where a horse and cart waited for him, threw himself onto it, and began to drive. He followed the McGregors' carriage, and so did several others carrying oblivious members of the crowd back to their homes. Bill could not afford to gallop, and neither could Holmes. After a maddeningly sedate few minutes, the other carriages began to pull off into side streets, and Holmes became concerned that he might have to change course quickly to avoid having his purpose detected.

Holmes's concern turned to relief when it

became apparent that the last two carriages between him and the McGregors had longer journeys than the others. He hung back, and as the four vehicles traveled further and further, he realised Barnett was doing exactly as he'd expected. One of the other two carriages finally turned onto a dirt road, and Holmes quietly followed its driver into the night.

In a few short minutes, the detective had doubled back and taken a totally different route out of town, into the long dark where the roads were hardly marked. As soon as he found himself alone, he urged the horse forward, as fast as it would go. He rode through the night, passing trees and hearing hooves beat the sandy ground, with no thought but his destination, cursing the necessity of taking the roundabout way. Thankfully, the horse was strong, and it kept up the fierce gallop that matched the pounding of the detective's heart.

He wondered if Irene realised what was happening to her. Of course she must, but she would be calm. The Woman wouldn't let her fear destroy her judgement. She would fight back, but Holmes didn't believe she would succeed, and as perverse as that thought felt as it came to him, he knew that she must not, or the plan would be incomplete. Three to two might be decent odds, but Holmes had seen the foreman's musculature and knew that he was strong, and while Barnett's physical strength was unknown, he would undoubtedly be carrying a gun to help him force obedience from his unwilling captives. Unless Tootie or Ambrose McGregor possessed unexpected skill, Holmes had little doubt the three would remain subdued by Barnett and Bill.

It felt all wrong somehow, to be on a different road than the one carrying the object of his concern and to be wishing that she and her companions would be held hostage instead of finding their way out of an impossible situation. He hoped that Barnett had planned well. He needed the man's plan to succeed partially before his could be fully effective.

After a long time, Holmes turned his horse onto a dirt road and followed it beyond a group of trees. He stopped and looked around, carefully seeking any sign of the presence of another human being, but no one else was present and no sounds could be heard except the calls of crickets and tree frogs. The detective alighted from his cart and went toward an unlocked door, ready for the next phase of the plan to commence. He took his place and waited, hoping devoutly that nothing had gone wrong along the way.

Holmes crouched, his every sense at the highest possible level of alertness, his mind filled with the calm that always came when a case was about to reach its climax. Watson never understood that calm, but it was the calm of a man waiting for events to unfold the way he'd pictured them and thinking through every possible contingency in order to avert it. After what felt like ages, he heard voices.

Chapter 15: Irene

Someone stole my gun during the theatre interval. I don't know how it happened, but one moment I was trying to keep Tootie from succumbing to claustrophobia, and the next I found my bag empty of its only important item. I forced myself to silence my self-flagellating brain and instead reason through the theft and whether it was more likely that my weapon was now in the hands of someone significant or a random pickpocket who had chosen to target theatregoers that night.

I wondered how Holmes would rate the likelihood of a coincidence. The idea that a woman who was involved in a criminal case would also be involved in a petty theft, randomly chosen out of a group of hundreds, hardly seemed creditable. I didn't appear noticeably richer or more opulently dressed than others in the crowd. Why choose me?

The other alternative was much more horrifying, but I forced myself to consider it. I ruled out Ambrose McGregor immediately because I had seen his whereabouts the whole time, and then I began to scan the crowd systematically, looking for anyone familiar. I found no one unexpected and finally had to take my seat again for the third act.

I remained outwardly calm throughout the rest of the play, but I felt as if a weight were pressing on my chest, making it hard to breathe. In some grotesque sense, Hedda Gabler's elaborately staged desperation seemed to mirror the growing desperation I felt. I now realised that it had been a mistake to come to the theatre. In public, I felt like a clay pigeon on display in a shooting gallery.

When the curtain finally closed, I wanted to escape the auditorium as soon as possible, but the crowd and Tootie's friendliness caused us to be one of the last groups to leave. Ambrose sent for our carriage, and I waited nervously, trying to answer Tootie's banal chatter but feeling as if I would like to run away.

Finally, the carriage arrived, and Ambrose glanced at the driver and commented that 'Bryce has sent someone else.' The McGregors rented a carriage for their use in Florida, and they hired drivers when they needed them. I thought nothing of the comment. Nothing, that is, until Ambrose had helped me inside and I saw Tootie's pale face, her words silenced by the cocked pistol at her temple. I looked over into the cold eyes of my solicitor. 'If you so much as call out, I'll pull the trigger,' he said matter-of-factly as Ambrose took his place beside me. I believed him.

At that moment, I understood why my handgun was gone and why the theft had been so expertly carried out. Excellent foresight on Barnett's part. The terror on Ambrose McGregor's face struck me as vastly ironic, a combination of genuine fear for his wife and horror at a friend's betrayal. His innocence was apparent, and in the midst of my fear, I felt the letdown of having been wrong, of having fallen for a classic red herring. Oh, how Dr Watson would enjoy the story if he ever had a chance to hear it, I thought wryly.

We rode in silence for some time until Barnett finally rested his hand on his knee with his gun pointed firmly at Ambrose. 'Why are you doing this?' the poor man finally asked, a question that even I had no real answer to as of yet, in spite of my part in the investigation.

Barnett, as Sanchez, smiled and addressed me instead. 'Do you know me, Miss Adler the Divine?'

I nodded, projecting as much calm as I could manage. 'I knew you from the moment the wife of the tobacco supplier laid eyes on you.'

He looked surprised for a moment, then smiled. 'I didn't envy her husband that day. Now I see that I was mistaken. But no matter. It's all worked out in the end.'

He finally turned to Ambrose, shaking his head. 'You're a good man, Mr McGregor. You and your wife have no reason to be afraid if you do as you're told. This operation (he looked at me) is about Miss Adler, myself, and Mr Holmes. Both Mr Holmes, if you like, but I only ever had the younger in mind as part of this particular plan.'

'I wouldn't do that, Miss Adler.' The gun was trained on me in a split second, and Barnett shook his head. 'It's no use inching your hand toward the door latch; at this speed, you'd fall out and injure your skull, not to mention that we're currently in the middle of nowhere.'

I wondered what Holmes would have done in this situation—in a closed carriage with a gunman and two innocent people. He'd have had a solution, I was sure, but I was at a loss, and it infuriated me.

'You might like to know,' Barnett continued, 'that my office in London received Irene Norton's new will today, leaving the bulk of her property to her faithful solicitor, who will transfer it to his good friend Alberto Sanchez as soon as Mrs Norton is dead.'

'But don't worry. I won't kill you if you sign over everything instead. The detective is the only one who has to die, and that's not my job.'

Tootie hadn't uttered a word since the beginning of the ordeal, and she still sat with her hands clenched, pale and terrified. I had never seen her silent for so long, and there was something grotesquely humorous about it. I hated myself for thinking so.

'Holmes isn't here,' I said. I considered saying something about his death, but I could see no use in doing so since Barnett knew very well that he was alive.

'No,' said Barnett, 'but he will be. You're excellent bait.'

At the word *bait*, something connected in my mind, and I understood. That was my role in the case. Holmes had been using me to attract Barnett the way the solicitor was now trying to use me to attract the detective. That was the reason for the lack of caution and insistence that I play a role so near my own character. Unwitting bait, that's what I'd been. And now that the bait had been taken, Holmes was nowhere to be found.

I wasn't angry with Holmes, but I was disappointed. For a short space of time, I had believed in him fully, trusting that he would complete his plan, whatever it might be. I had also trusted his promise of safety. *Bait is never safe* I thought bitterly. Whatever Holmes had expected to happen, the current situation was obviously far from it, I knew, or I wouldn't have found myself stranded in a carriage with a criminal and no recourse. The man I had fooled once had made another mistake, and this time it was to my extreme detriment.

'I have no idea,' Barnett continued after a few moments, 'if you and Holmes are working together, and I don't care. Either way, he'll follow you.'

'How do you know he's in Florida?' I asked, thinking quickly. If Barnett didn't know for sure that I'd been working with Holmes, then I had the upper hand of information, at least.

'I saw him two weeks ago,' he said. 'He's tracked you, I'm sure, whether you know it or not. Also, thank you for the calling cards, my dear. It would have taken me much longer to realise you were here and might be in society tonight without them. I don't have the slightest idea what you hoped to accomplish, but I'm glad I circumvented it.' He smiled nastily.

I also had no idea what I'd hoped to accomplish or, indeed, what he was talking about, so I kept my thoughts to myself and tried to look upset at being thwarted, which wasn't difficult, since I was frightened and angry.

Finally, our miserable journey ended with an abrupt stop, and Barnett herded the three of us outside into the dark night. I realised immediately where we were when I smelt the sharp aroma of citrus in the air and turned and saw the shack in front of us, the ramshackle building that contained Alberto Sanchez's field office.

The driver hopped down and took off his hat, revealing himself to be Bill, the surly foreman Holmes and I had met during our previous visit. He took out a handgun and pointed it in our direction, helping his boss force us inside.

The shed was dark, but Sanchez lit a lantern and pushed us into his office. Ambrose gave the two chairs to Tootie and I, and he stood, his face dark. Bill stood watch in the front of the building, and Sanchez sat behind his desk, staring at his captives with gun in hand.

'What do you intend to do?' I asked, hoping to hear something I might be able to use.

'I intend to wait until Sherlock Holmes arrives, release our friends, get a signed statement from you giving me your assets, and take the detective to the lighthouse,' he said, with a chilling lack of hesitation.

'Why do you want Holmes?'

'I don't want him, but Sebastian Moran does. He's meant to be dead—Holmes, I mean. I have no idea why he isn't, but Moran knew right away. It's a good deal for me, Miss A. You've always been a good client, and I don't want to hurt you. That's why I'm going to leave you enough money to go wherever you like.'

'What's the benefit to you? I know very well you don't do anything without getting something back.'

He laughed. 'You know me well, Miss Adler. The convenient part of this plan is that the bait is also the prize. In return for Holmes, I get to keep your fortune.'

'You have a loose tongue,' Ambrose suddenly put in quietly, his face stormy.

I turned to the McGregors. 'You deserve

to know that this man is no more Alberto Sanchez than I am. He's a crooked London solicitor named James Barnett.' Tootie's eyes widened.

'How do you know him?' Ambrose's meaning was clear; he thought I was in league with Barnett.

'I was stupid enough to let him handle my affairs,' I said honestly.

'Far too few affairs,' said Barnett, with an ugly insinuation in his voice, 'but plenty of money.'

'Holmes won't come,' I said. 'He has no idea I'm here, and if he did, he wouldn't care.'

'You're wrong there, Miss A.' Barnett sat back and folded his hands over his stomach, looking self-satisfied. 'I've no doubt he's on his way right now.'

'If that's true,' I said, 'how do you know he won't bring the police?' I stared him down.

'Doesn't matter if he does. They'll let me go to save you three. I didn't take the McGregors for no reason. Bill and I will be happy to fill any of them with lead, though, if they try anything.' He turned to Ambrose. 'You, at least, should know that Sherlock Holmes is on the way.'

Ambrose shook his head. 'It appears I haven't been very smart about all this. Whatever happens, please accept my apologies, Miss Adler.'

'That's all right,' I said, trying to smile. 'I did

159

lie about my identity.'

'I knew there was something more to you than a simple socialite,' Tootie's voice suddenly cut in. 'I don't know who you are, but I'm not surprised.'

'I'm sorry,' I said without explanation, seeing no reason to give Barnett more information than he already had.

'It's all right,' she said unexpectedly. 'We're all more than we seem.'

'That's certainly true,' said Barnett, pulling a handkerchief out of his pocket. 'I should give this back to you, Miss A.' I looked at the piece of cloth, a white background with blue letters. Mine. I took it without comment.

I was disappointed in myself. I'd always imagined that if I were in mortal danger, I'd be resourceful and fearless, able to think my way out of anything. But I was just Irene Adler, frozen in the face of danger the way I'd been powerless to stop my husband.

'I suppose I should have you sign the papers before Holmes gets here,' said Barnett after a while. 'Things might get ugly, and I want to have everything in place.' His calmness infuriated me.

The solicitor produced a stack of legal forms, the paper that represented my not-insignificant worldly property. 'Sign these, or I'll put a bullet in your head,' he said calmly. I stared down at them, my eyes swimming.

Just then, Alberto Sanchez's desk took on a

life of its own and flew forward, crashing to the floor as I jumped backward to avoid its path.

Chapter 16: Holmes

Sherlock Holmes rushed to his feet and tackled James Barnett, his long-constricted muscles screaming from the sudden exercise. The altercation was over in seconds, the shocked Barnett clumsy and slow in his surprise. Holmes pushed his gun against the man's head as Bill rushed into the office, astonished by the crash.

'Nice to see you, Mr Holmes.' He touched his forelock in respect to the detective.

Holmes laughed noiselessly. 'Thank you for your assistance, Mr Waverly. I'll put in a good word with my brother.' The detective noticed Irene's pale, unreadable face watching him attentively.

'Miss Adler, I have something that belongs to you.' He took The Woman's gun from his waistband and handed it to her, smiling. She took it with a blank expression.

'Allow me to introduce myself, Sir and Madam. I am Sherlock Holmes, consulting detective,' said Holmes, turning to the McGregors, who looked dazed. 'I believe, Sir, that there has been a misunderstanding, for which I apologise.' His eyes took in Ambrose, who bowed his head slightly.

'Not at all, Mr Holmes. I now comprehend that my wife and I have been mixed up in something far larger than we realised.'

'I'm grateful to have two such reliable witnesses to this man's intentions,' the detective replied, indicating the furious Barnett, whose face under his makeup was a violent shade of red.

'Will we have to testify in court?' asked Tootie, suddenly finding her voice again.

'Indeed, Madam, I would expect so,' Holmes answered with a smile. 'I hope it won't be overly distressing.'

'Not at all,' said the lady, looking almost pleased, her equilibrium apparently returning. She moved to her husband's side, and he put an arm about her.

Holmes looked at The Woman, wondering about her thoughts. He had never seen her so pale, but otherwise, she looked perfectly composed. 'Miss Adler,' he said after a moment, 'I believe our friends have arrived. Please be so kind as to usher them inside.' His keen ears had detected the sound of more than wind approaching, and soon voices and boots could be heard. Irene went outside, and no one spoke until the door of the shed was forcefully pushed open and a stocky policeman entered, followed by Thomas Edison, who looked characteristically calm, and little Nelson Burroughs, who was attempting to look fierce. Irene followed last, still looking somewhat dazed.

'Welcome, Gentlemen,' said Holmes, standing up straight and nodding to the newcomers.

'I'm Sheriff Samuel Morris,' said the solid, middle-aged officer of the law. 'I assume you're Mr Sherlock Holmes, detective of London.'

'I am indeed,' said Holmes quietly.

'And this is Miss Irene Adler, legally Mrs Norton, subject of a plot put forth by the gentleman here, Mr James Barnett, known locally as Alberto Sanchez.'

'That is correct, Sir,' answered the detective. 'I'm afraid we haven't time for conversation. This man's associates, under the orders of a criminal named Sebastian Moran, are even now awaiting the delivery of my person. We have a chance of apprehending them if we move in haste.'

Thankfully, Holmes realised, the policeman wasn't as slow as some of his counterparts across the Atlantic. He immediately produced handcuffs, which Holmes assisted him in placing on the surly suspect, then led the entire group outside. His quickly-uttered 'What do you propose to do, Mr Holmes?' endeared him eternally to the detective.

'Mr and Mrs McGregor, Mr Thomas Edison will take you home in your carriage. You've been through plenty of surprises this evening,' the detective began. 'Miss Adler, you will accompany me and our friend Barnett in my cart, with Sheriff Morris and Mr Burroughs following behind. We've no time to lose.'

Holmes was relieved when everyone did exactly as they were told, moving rapidly, propelled by the force of his personality. He used his gun to push Barnett forward, and Irene followed to where his cart was hidden in the darkness, his horse tethered to a tree. Irene trained her gun on the solicitor while Holmes freed the horse and prepared to drive. As he had anticipated, Bill was nowhere to be found, as if he'd melted into the night. No doubt, Holmes knew, he'd resurface wherever he was assigned.

The detective watched The Woman force Barnett into the cart. Holmes wondered what the man was about. He was too quiescent, and Holmes had every belief that he was plotting something, but The Woman could handle him, at least until they reached the beach. The detective drove quickly, and his horse, rested from its long wait, was delighted to run. Holmes was optimistic, pleased with Irene's perfect handling of her difficult role and with the outcome. Barnett had been entirely fooled, both by Bill, Mycroft's agent, and by Miss A, who had been magnificent both intentionally and unintentionally. The night was far from over, but he knew now that he was in control.

The oppressive darkness, punctuated by

moonlight, was almost like a living thing as the detective drove the cart to the coast, with the clop of the police horse behind, reminding him that the law and the young Burroughs were with him, ready to provide backup. Holmes didn't know exactly what they would find at the drop-off point. He hardly hoped to nab Moran; unlikely the man would have made the journey himself. Instead, they would most likely capture a few of the mid-level operatives from Moriarty's vast but splintering organisation. At any rate, capturing any of them would be a positive outcome, especially if it could be accomplished without bloodshed. He was well aware that the situation was likely to be complicated.

'If you move again, I'll put a bullet in your leg.' Holmes heard Irene's voice, calm and deadly, break into his thoughts.

'You've never shot anyone,' rejoined the solicitor derisively.

'No, but I'm the sort of person who could.'

After that, silence reigned, but Holmes glanced behind him to ascertain that all was well. The Woman looked oddly peaceful, her gun resting on her lap, pointed squarely at Barnett, who sat still with his hands cuffed. Holmes smiled to himself. Irene was all right. She wouldn't be taken by surprise.

*　　　*　　　*

The coastline was eerily beautiful in the moonlight. Holmes had heard a local rumour that pirates had once patrolled these waters, quartering captives on an island nearby. He could well believe it. What was idyllic in daylight had a savage edge in the nighttime.

Holmes drove until he saw a lighthouse in the distance, giving off a faint glow. He stopped his horse at the edge of the sand and jumped down as the policeman halted his own cart. Catching glimpses of Irene's face, Holmes saw that she was relieved that the long ride spent staring at the solicitor was complete. He trained his gun on the man as Morris and Burroughs joined them.

'You see the lighthouse,' the detective said quickly. 'No doubt they have a boat waiting to carry them out to sea as soon as the drop has been made. I gather that's how Mr Barnett was to get out of the country as well.' He looked at the solicitor, 'If you'd like to confirm that, it wouldn't go amiss.' Angry eyes stared back at him.

'Here is what must happen now. One of you will impersonate Mr Sanchez and follow me to the lighthouse, after which the others will wait until we start for the boat and converge with us there, in order to capture not only those on land, but also those who may be waiting on the water.

'Needless to say,' he continued, 'this is a risk, but not as much as it would be if our solicitor friend were involved. Sheriff Morris, I must ask you to remove the man's jacket.' Morris stared at Holmes briefly before taking off the solicitor's handcuffs. For a moment, Barnett looked as if he might make some sort of attempt to fight, but the joint effect of Irene's and Holmes's guns on him, as well as the beefy arms of the policeman, kept him subdued. Burroughs's eyes were enormous with confusion.

'Irene,' said Holmes, once he held the jacket in his hand, 'I believe you're the only one who will suffice. Mr Burroughs is too short and Sheriff Morris too robust.' The Woman looked surprised, but she comprehended his meaning and took Barnett's evening jacket from the policeman, putting it on and using it to cover her figure. 'Now, Mr Burroughs, your hat.' Burroughs was frozen for a moment, as if he hadn't heard, then removed his highly fashionable hat and handed it to Holmes, who placed it on Irene's head, hiding her hair. The Woman looked up at him with a roguish smile that passed in a second. 'The darkness will hide your dress long enough for my purposes,' the detective added, noting that Irene looked relieved. She appeared to have wondered if he intended her to exchange clothes completely with the solicitor.

Holmes handed his gun to Burroughs, who stared at it as if it were some kind of ferocious animal in his hand. 'Sheriff Morris and Mr Burroughs,' the detective continued, 'I trust you will take care of our friend while Miss Adler and I begin the operation. A gag might be in order to keep him from making noise. Once we're ready to rendezvous, Mr Burroughs can keep his gun on the prisoner while Sheriff Morris helps us subdue the others.' He helped the policeman re-cuff the solicitor, who spit in his face. Holmes merely wiped his cheek and didn't deign to reply.

'Now, Irene,' he said, turning his back to her, 'please be so good as to jam the barrel of your pistol into the small of my back, and we will proceed.' Irene did as he asked, none too gently, and he began the walk across the sand to the blur in the distance that was the lighthouse. Behind him, he heard muffled curses and the calm voice of the policeman, noises indicating that he had taken Holmes's advice and decided to gag the prisoner to prevent him somehow giving them away by shouting. *Not entirely stupid*, thought Holmes, gratified.

'Are you all right?' the detective finally asked in a low voice as he and Irene made their way across the wide expanse of sand.

'Tolerably,' she answered.

'You won't have to speak. I'll make sure of that.'

'Very well.'

'Remain in the shadows and stay behind me, and I'll keep you from being detected until the men emerge and we make for the boat. Morris will join us then.'

Holmes continued, 'Just keep your head down and don't be afraid to use your weapon if things don't go to plan. We're taking a risk, but I don't wish to lose any of the perpetrators.'

'No more do I,' Irene answered. 'At least Morris doesn't seem a complete fool. He'll come to our aid if he sees or hears anything amiss. Have you any idea how many are in the lighthouse?'

'A few at the most. More would have attracted local attention, and Moran has to allocate his resources carefully these days. The Yard have been on him heavily since Moriarty's death. His outsized faith in Barnett results from the man's previous service to the organisation, I gather.'

'What previous service?'

'That I do not know. Even Mycroft's people hadn't uncovered it at the time of his last letter.'

It was odd, Holmes thought, to be conversing with The Woman in an almost enjoyable way under the present circumstances. Watson was nearly silent at these times. With his back to Irene, the detective couldn't see her face, but their words flowed back and forth as usual, and she sounded strangely normal. He wondered how the evening's events were affecting her, how long it would be before her adrenaline gave way to weariness. He hoped she would be able to stay with him, to keep her senses keen, until after it was all over. He needed her mind to be clear.

Both fell silent for several moments. As they drew closer to their destination, Holmes heard Irene's breathing quicken. 'Steady on,' he whispered.

The structure itself had the usual appearance of a coastal lighthouse, tall and sturdy with a large door in its side. He hoped the men had a reliable lookout and were not waiting for some prearranged signal from Sanchez. That would, he thought, be inconvenient. The detective raised his arms and gesticulated as they came close, giving the appearance of a man under great duress.

Holmes's wish was granted a few feet from the lighthouse, when he heard a male voice shout and saw a man appear at the door, brandishing a rifle. 'There's no need to be dramatic,' the detective said loudly but icily, 'Mr Sanchez's gun in my spine speaks loudly enough.' Two men came out the door and faced Holmes, who kept his thin body squarely in front of Irene in order to shield her from view as much as possible in the moonlight.

'A gentleman might think it unsporting to capture a man by dressing as a lady,' said Holmes in an indignant tone, hoping to buy a few more moments by selling Irene's unexpected attire.

One of the men, who was tall and young, let out a hearty laugh. 'Didn't expect such creativity from you, Mr Barnett. Moran told us you were a by-the-book man.'

Excellent, thought Holmes, they hadn't met Barnett. Irene stayed silent, as he'd instructed. 'Oh, he's plenty creative,' he said, sounding angry.

'Be quiet,' said the other man, who was of middle age and seemed jumpy. 'Let's get to the boat before Sammy falls asleep.'

Holmes saw movement out of the corner of his eye, and suddenly Barnett came rushing toward them, yelling against his gag. The detective was forced to move, revealing Irene. The young man from the lighthouse immediately grabbed her gun. At the same time, Holmes pinned the hysterical Barnett on the ground while the older man trained his gun on the detective's temple.

At that moment, Morris and Burroughs burst toward the group, and confusion reigned. Morris tackled the older man, and Burroughs stood at the edge, looking bewildered. Finally, the voice of the younger lookout cut through the madness. 'This is all well and good, Mr Holmes, but if you don't come with us, I'll shoot the head off the la—' A deafening, close-range shot rang out, and he lurched forward, blood beginning to spurt from his mouth; he was dead almost instantly. Immediately, Irene jerked the gun from his hand and pointed it at Barnett, while Morris dragged the older accomplice to his feet. Burroughs stood behind Irene, his face deathly white, with a painfully hot gun in his shaking hand.

His pistol firmly trained on his prisoner, Morris looked gratefully at the bewildered Burroughs. 'Well done, Sir,' he said. 'I hope you still intend to make this town your home one day.' The small man didn't answer, but his colour slowly returned.

Holmes hauled up Barnett, who was practically foaming at the mouth in rage. 'As I said a few moments ago,' the detective intoned calmly, 'there's no need to be dramatic.'

Morris put a hand on the detective's shoulder. 'I'm afraid we've lost the boat, Mr Holmes.' Sure enough, in the beginning half-light, Holmes saw the outline of a small craft moving further away from the Florida coast each moment. It was a pity, but not a contingency he'd seen as particularly unlikely.

'It's all right. I'll alert the proper authorities.' He meant Mycroft, but saw no need for a lengthy explanation. Sammy, whoever he was, would be long gone before the American authorities could track him. Morris nodded, and Holmes was surprised once again at the man's sense. Lestrade could afford to learn from him, the detective thought.

'I'll send the boys out for the body,' said the policeman after a moment. The corpse looked

172

vulnerable in the dawning light, nothing like the surly young man who'd threatened to kill Irene Adler.

Holmes led the way, and Irene, Burroughs, and Morris herded Barnett and the other man toward the wagons and impatient horses. Without a second pair of handcuffs, the policeman was forced to tie the older man's hands with twine found in the bottom of one of the wagons, a task he seemed to enjoy. He took charge of both prisoners, with Burroughs, less shaky than before, consenting to drive the police wagon. To Holmes's surprise, Irene waited at the front of the other cart until he helped her up next to the driver's seat, which he filled himself. He took the reins, relief beginning to settle over him. Both he and The Woman were safe.

Chapter 17: Irene

I was comfortable beside the detective. For the moment, that was enough. It was too soon for the anxieties of the previous days to leave me or for my mind to make sense of all the twisted threads that had entwined to create the events of the evening. I just was. I smelt the smell of the water and sand in the early morning, felt the breeze and the brush of trees as we made our way back to the road, and enjoyed the presence of another human being.

I am Irene Adler, I thought. Not Irene Norton or some combination of the two. Just Irene Adler. It was a deconstructed feeling, but I didn't mind. I felt lighter, almost as if Barnett had succeeded in taking everything from me and I didn't care. He had shown me my life with nothing, and the vision hadn't destroyed me. Now that I once again possessed all that was mine, my grasp felt stronger and lighter at the same time. Even if everything in the whole world was taken from me, I would not break, and I would not die.

After a long silence in the warm autumn morning, Holmes turned to me. 'My shoulder is not the most congenial of pillows, but I have no objection to its use,' he said quietly. I realised that I was exhausted, bone-tired from danger and exertion and too little sleep. I wondered how Holmes managed to keep his eyes open, but I drifted to sleep leaning against him before I could finish the thought.

I awoke as Holmes stopped the horse in front of the police station and jail, a tiny building in the middle of town, situated next to the home of the volunteer fire brigade, judging by the accoutrements lying about. I watched sleepily as Morris and Burroughs pushed the unhappy Barnett and the older man inside, then waited for Holmes to help me down. I was too disorientated from sleep to climb, so he proffered his arms instead, and I put my hands on his shoulders. His long fingers around my waist were warm and strong as he effortlessly swung me down and placed me on solid ground, smiling down at me. I saw that his eyes were closing with weariness and that his face, always almost painful in its thinness, was gaunt.

Inside his own kingdom, Morris was all business. He imprisoned the two men quickly, doing the necessary paperwork to start the state's process, then sent a boy who was loitering in the street to collect his part-time deputies, brothers who worked as carpenters in their father's shop. In the meantime, he produced adequate coffee, which he gave to all, including Barnett and the other man, who claimed to be named Joshua Mason. Now that the guilty were contained, I noted that Morris had the quality of many a good policeman, human objectivity that boggles the mind, that can put aside terrible acts of even moments before and treat the guilty simply as human beings—human beings in limbo, but human beings nonetheless. Holmes also possessed this quality, but I did not.

I could not yet look at Barnett or Mason with any objectivity. My eyes were clouded by the sight of the dead man and the horror in Nelson Burroughs's eyes at having killed him, the terror that silenced the gregarious tongue of Tootie McGregor, and for myself, the feeling of claustrophobic danger that had all-too-poignantly recalled my life with my husband. Perhaps some day, not far off, I would be thankful for what I had learned about myself, but I could not feel grateful yet, and the sight of the criminals turned my stomach.

My faculties had once again become reasonably alert from movement and coffee once the Bartholomew brothers arrived, strapping young men who each had at least half a foot over their boss. 'Good morning, Sir,' they said deferentially, almost in unison, and I realised they were twins. Morris told them where to find the body, and they went off eagerly, apparently glad for some actual police business to attend to. Fort Myers didn't seem to be a hotbed of illegal activity, especially not the sort that concerned more than one country.

Deputies dispatched, Morris set about taking statements, choosing out of his own kindness to begin with Burroughs. With a gently businesslike manner, he ushered the still-shaken young man into a tiny back room, while Holmes and I drank second and third cups of coffee in the front of the station. I was glad we were removed from Barnett and Mason, even if only by a thin wall. I had no desire to see the solicitor's face again.

'My brother will take care of getting your assets into the proper order if you wish,' said Holmes after a while. 'Otherwise, I fear you may face undue delays in recovering them.'

'Thank you, Holmes,' I answered, wanting to say more but unsure how to begin.

'Our solicitor is very discreet,' he added. I nodded in acquiescence.

At once it struck me how odd it was to be drinking coffee with the detective again, but to feel so differently. Only a few days had passed since our memorable meeting in my dressing room, a meeting of seemingly disparate minds united by a single piece of paper and two names that had turned out to be one. But we had never really been dissimilar, Holmes and I. The case had shown me that the hints of things I'd discovered about the detective during our last interaction—trustworthy, kind things— were far stronger parts of him than people realised. Neither of us was soft; we were both honed edges that could cut in an instant, but if we were sharp, we were also straight.

After half an hour had passed, Morris and Burroughs emerged, and the policeman clapped Burroughs on the shoulder. 'You're a true hero, Mr Burroughs, and I hope you won't let this unfortunate incident cloud your view of our city.'

Burroughs looked at us all with relief on his face. 'Just glad I could help, Sir, Mr Holmes, Mrs, I mean—'

'Miss Adler,' I supplied with a smile, and he smiled back.

'You'll be called to testify, Mr Burroughs,

and I wouldn't be surprised if the mayor sees fit to give you a commendation,' said the policeman with finality. The young man nodded and left the station, but I didn't think any mayor's commendation would be sufficient to compensate him for what he'd been through.

Once Burroughs was gone, Morris turned to me, and I noticed that in spite of all the events of the nighttime, his brown hair was still perfectly coiffed. 'I'd like to get your statement now, if you don't mind, Miss Adler.' I didn't mind, but Holmes put a hand on my arm as I started to get up.

'Sheriff Morris, I'd be grateful if you'd let Miss Adler and I give statements together. I realise it's slightly irregular, but given enough time, I could produce permission from as high as you'd like.'

The policeman sat back down and seemed to be contemplating how much he trusted Sherlock Holmes. 'Very well,' he finally said, 'I know there's more to this than meets the eye. There was that fellow Bill, the one who alerted me, for one thing. He had identification from a government organisation I won't mention.'

'Very wise,' Holmes put in.

'Here's the thing,' said Morris, looking at both of us. 'I have a dead body to account for. What I want are statements that explain it. I'm not fool enough to think the entire case, whatever it entails, is under my jurisdiction.'

'What we need, Sir,' I put in, 'is for Holmes to be nonexistent in this case.' The policeman raised one eyebrow, a signal that he was about to become obstinate.

'Give me twenty-four hours, and I will have all the reasons you need to keep me out of it,' said Holmes.

The policeman nodded abruptly. 'I trust you, Mr Holmes, but for this, I need solid proof. I'll give you the day you request.'

'Understandable,' I murmured, and I noticed that the detective didn't seem perturbed either. I wondered if he meant to flee.

I couldn't help feeling a little bit of regret at leaving Morris without a satisfactory explanation, but as soon as Holmes and I emerged into the sunshine, my spirits lifted. It was fully daytime now, and people were about in the streets, shopping and working. I looked around, and the city of Fort Myers looked different, friendlier, without the spectre of an enemy hanging over my head.

Holmes re-hitched the wagon. 'I was thinking, Mrs James,' he said playfully, 'that perhaps it might behove us to use the hotel instead of the flat above Sloane's General Store, now that we have our choice.'

I laughed, and we made our way back to the Keystone. My opulent room seemed far removed from all the things that had happened to me since I had been in it, but there it was when I returned, just as I had left it. Holmes appealed to the office for his own room and was given one adjacent to mine.

My companion did not bother to close the door between our rooms before sprawling across his bed and falling into a much-needed sleep. In a reversal of our former positions, I sat by the window and watched him, and I wondered if he had also watched me in a similar way. In sleep, all of his strength and control were gone, and he was simply a man. I realised in that moment that I had become his friend.

Holmes slept for three hours, and I spent them in contemplation, examining my feelings one by one and trying to put to rest as many as I could. I had never been so near death before, and I found that I was different afterward—calmer, less afraid that the world would pass me by, and happier just to be in it. Time would tell how far that difference went.

Holmes finally awoke in the late morning and came into my room, instantly alert. 'You look better,' I commented. 'Better still with food.'

'Agreed,' he said simply, so I had some brought up, soup that tasted canned, a beef dish with noodles that the hotel called 'stroganoff,' and a bakewell pudding at the end. Both of us ate with abandon and determination. I had read Dr Watson's descriptions of the succulent dinners he and

Holmes sometimes enjoyed, but I'd never actually seen Holmes eat heartily before. With amusement, I realised the accounts weren't lies after all. The detective was quite capable of taking in energy when he needed it.

Once finished, Holmes perched on the ancient divan in my room and gazed at me with an uncertain expression. 'I feel I owe you some explanation of the events of the past few days.' I met his eyes, and he looked away, almost as if he were avoiding the intimacy.

'After you recognised the solicitor, I began to suspect where matters stood. If harming or capturing me had been the man's sole object, it would have made little sense for him not to have devised a way to entrap me the night we first met. He had a decided advantage since he knew my face, but I did not know his. He would, at least, have had a good chance. As it was, I knew he must be waiting for something else. The presence of the letter pointed two ways, to you by its content and to Mycroft by the ease with which it was procured and the presence of the photograph in Sanchez's office. I couldn't dismiss the notion that if the man knew my brother well enough to target him, he would also know what an impossible target my brother would be. The Florida connection would have been senseless in that situation. As a result, I began to be convinced that you were as much a target as I, if not more.

'That's why I insisted that we separate. I realised that the man knew of my presence but did not appear to know of yours. I surmised that he'd known you were coming to Florida for your singing tour and assumed that I would follow Sanchez here, but he didn't seem to know that we were together and both in Fort Myers. I decided to force him to make a move.'

'That's why you used me as bait,' I put in.

'Yes, I—' For once, the detective looked as if he were at a loss. 'I understand that it caused you a vast amount of—unpleasantness—' he trailed off. It was the least fluent speech I'd ever heard him give.

I rose from my chair and went to him. 'Get up, Holmes,' I said forcefully, hoping to startle him into obedience. He did as I asked, his tall frame dwarfing mine once he was standing.

'Thank you,' I said, and I stood on my toes and wrapped my arms around his neck, holding him tightly for a few seconds. When I pulled back, he looked more shocked than I'd ever seen him. I returned to my chair, but he seemed entirely unable to speak for quite a while, sitting on the edge of the divan with a bewildered face.

'I'm afraid the logic of this situation escapes me, Irene,' he finally managed, which caused me to laugh uproariously for some time, while he stared at me as if I'd gone mad.

'Please continue your tale, Holmes,' I finally

182

sputtered. I breathed deeply for a moment and gathered my wits again. 'I simply wished to express my thanks for your rescue and my lack of anger all at once. That seemed the simplest way.' I gave him what can only be described as a coy look, which he received with a raised eyebrow.

'Very well,' he said, looking at his hands. 'While you were living the somewhat frustrating life of Lavinia James, abandoned by her business-bound husband, I was busy. I visited Sanchez's grove office, his town office, and his home.' I looked up in surprise. This I had certainly not expected.

'I left the man three items: a handkerchief embroidered with IN, a lady's powder box, and a calling card. These things, of course, were meant to make him believe that Irene Adler was indeed in Fort Myers and was on to him. My additional hope was that if he thought you responsible for these tokens, he would not realise the two of us were working in unison, as he apparently did not.'

'Well, that explains one of the mysteries,' I said, remembering Barnett's comments about my helpful calling cards. 'Nicely done, Holmes. I'd not have thought to taunt him in that way.'

'It was expedient,' Holmes answered quickly, 'an irresistible temptation to act, but it allowed him time to contact his associates and arrange the dropoff. He was most likely aware that Bernard James had disappeared, but he is not a stupid man, and his familiarity with me no doubt kept him from assuming I'd actually gone.

'Now we reach movements of mine that you do not know. The day you visited Tootie and Ambrose McGregor, I followed you. I will readily admit that I wanted to make sure you were following the plan, but,' he looked at me steadily, 'I was also concerned for your safety. Satisfied that you were with the McGregors, whom I did not believe to be part of the plot in spite of all of Ambrose's quiet discomfort, I continued my errands. I believe you may have seen me, hidden behind a copy of the *Ft. Myers Press.*'

I shook my head in annoyance at myself. Sure enough, I had seen the man, but since he'd made no effort to follow me, or so I thought, I'd dismissed him. 'Expertly carried out,' I said with a wry laugh.

'That afternoon,' Holmes continued, 'I returned to the store to wait for the evening, at which time I planned to pay Barnett's home a visit, which I later did. Before that, however, I received a visitor.'

'Bill,' I put in. I wanted to remind Holmes that I wasn't a complete fool, whatever my lack of observation of him might have suggested. He smiled appreciatively.

'Exactly so. It had taken him my two visits and a critical look at the photograph his boss possessed to understand who I was. Our disguises fooled Barnett, but Bill, or whatever his real name is, figured us out after we had made our exit. I was not entirely surprised to see him, or, rather, to see an emissary of my brother. Mycroft had sent him here as soon as he'd first received Barnett's letter to Sanchez—strange to contemplate now—and Bill had insinuated himself into Sanchez's organisation. He had been told to expect me, but since he didn't move in the polite circles of his boss, he was not able to find me as quickly as the solicitor was fortunate enough to do. Barnett never mentioned that he'd met me at the Edisons' party, so Bill was left on his own. Fortunately, he put the pieces together and finally approached me that day, meeting me at the store on the pretext of doing an errand for his boss in town. He showed me identification that proved his claims, and I explained the situation to him. We agreed that Barnett was unlikely to wait long to act once he realised you were taunting him. Bill promised to help me, but we could not make firm plans without knowing how the solicitor would act.

'That night, you came to see me.' I looked away from him then. The memory was painful. Thinking back, I couldn't fault myself for my anger, but I also couldn't praise myself. I had acted according to my understanding at the time; that was all. 'Don't trouble yourself,' he continued, correctly interpreting my expression. 'Your distress made me strongly consider the downside of the plan, but I still considered it essential that you be as innocent as possible. When one is aware of such an operation, it is nearly impossible to act completely normally. Forgive me for the observation, but your relative lack of experience in these matters also made me wary of giving you more information that would require you to be deceptive. You had shown yourself to be an admirable actress, but I didn't want to tax your powers any more than necessary. I needed Barnett to think he had taken you completely by surprise, and the best way to accomplish it was for you to feel the part you had to play.' The detective spoke quickly and avoided my eyes again, as if he was afraid of the response he might receive.

'I agree with you,' I said quickly, to put his discomfort to an end. 'I was afraid, as afraid as Godfrey ever made me, but I see now the value of that fear. It was like a lullaby to soothe Barnett into thinking everything had gone as he expected. Had I known you were already in place, I doubt I'd have been able to act so convincingly.' I nodded to Holmes, and he nodded back, relieved.

'At the theatre that night—'

'—You stole my pistol,' I interrupted, smiling. 'You can imagine what a turn that gave me.'

'Indeed,' Holmes replied. 'I knew it would severely risk our ability to thwart the whole operation if you succeeded in getting yourself and the McGregors away from Barnett prematurely. I didn't yet know if he planned to act that night, but I expected it. I apologise for the theft. It felt ungentlemanly at the time and still seems so now, though I consider it to have been necessary.'

'Not at all,' I answered, 'though I did curse the thief roundly to myself.'

'If curses had power, one would think I'd be dead from all the lurid ones that have been directed at me by various persons,' Holmes said absently.

'Let me tell you something for a moment, Holmes,' I said, suddenly remembering that I, too, knew the solution to a small mystery. 'You were right about Marion Edison.'

'Oh?'

'She met the German lieutenant during an apparently heinous trip to Europe, but the attachment endured. He's here visiting, and now the young lady is trying to figure out how to break the news that they'd like to marry.' After a moment I added, 'She came to see me yesterday morning.'

'I know,' said Holmes quietly.

'Indeed?' I was intrigued.

'I am aware of all of your movements of that day,' he said, which was enough of an explanation for me to understand what he meant.

'Thank you,' I said simply.

'Not at all.' He coughed quietly, as if to change the subject, and continued. 'I considered the theatre a likely place for Barnett to act for a number of reasons, but I saw nothing amiss until after the interval. You noticed, I believe, that he was not in the audience before that.'

'Yes.'

'After I had relieved you of your weapon, I realised Barnett had joined us at the beginning of the second half, though I believe that fact eluded you. My subsequent movements made me nearly unable to keep myself from being seen by you. You have a very vigilant eye, Irene. Barnett would not have escaped it if you had been unencumbered by your hostess.' I grinned inadvertently as he went on. 'I thought I had been mistaken when it appeared that you and the McGregors would be safely conducted home in your carriage, but just before you left, I recognised that Bill was the driver, as he intended me to do. He gave me a nod, and I knew that his boss's plan was fully in motion. That nod also signaled that he had summoned the police, as he had promised he would do during our previous meeting. I had put a large store of trust in the man, but my brother's operatives are as trustworthy as he is.'

Even though I knew the order of events after that, I found myself eager to hear them. In my mind, I could see myself and the McGregors entering the carriage and losing hope, but now I could also see Holmes, watching over us. It seemed silly now to remember how sure I'd been that he'd failed.

'I followed your carriage in my cart for as long as I could without attracting attention, until I was sure Bill was making for the citrus grove. Then I made my way there as fast as I could, staying off the main roads. I arrived several moments before you did and took my place under Sanchez's desk, grateful for the sense of grandiosity that had prompted him to purchase such a large one. I still considered that you and the McGregors might have managed to overpower Barnett, but Bill was sworn to his role and had promised to help his boss if you began to succeed in taking him down. I needed his plan to remain intact in order to hear enough information to convict the man and lead us to his associates.

'You played your part brilliantly, as did the McGregors, and I waited, hoping to hear enough to bring Barnett down without waiting long enough to endanger you or your companions. Bill stood by to assist if anything began to go wrong. A very useful man, I must say. I also hoped the police would not arrive too early. Bill had instructed Sheriff Morris to take his time, and he had agreed, though not without some concern. Thankfully, by the time Barnett decided to force you to sign his very unfortunate papers, I had heard plenty. That, of course, was when I emerged.'

Chapter 18: Holmes

The detective couldn't help his enjoyment of the delight on Irene's face when he said the word *emerged*. He knew she was remembering the moment and probably experiencing once again the relief of knowing she hadn't been abandoned to a nasty fate. She had surprised him many times during their long conversation. He'd expected to have to explain himself, to have to apologise, but instead, she understood. She didn't even act as if she'd forgiven him; she acted as if she found nothing to forgive. He found it comforting to know that The Woman was so eminently reasonable, even when she'd been through so much.

He stopped speaking, his part of the tale concluded, and the two associates sat looking at each other in silence, enjoying one another's company and understanding. 'For the most part, a very successful case, Irene,' he said at last.

'Yes,' she answered, 'though it's a pity about Burroughs and the dead man and Sammy, whoever he is.'

'True,' he replied.

'You couldn't have done it without me.'

Irene's expression was teasing and playful.

'That, Miss Adler,' he answered, leaning toward her, 'is most certainly true.'

*   *   *

The middle part of the day was spent in sending a telegram to Mycroft, using the shorthand code the brothers had worked out years before, and taking tea while waiting for a response, which came promptly. It contained a set of words and names Holmes didn't recognise but assumed Sheriff Morris would, since its function was to convince him to expunge all mention of Sherlock Holmes from his record of the case.

'You intend to cooperate with Morris, then?' Irene asked, as the two left the telegraph office with the message in hand.

'Of course,' said Holmes.

'I thought perhaps you meant to leave without a trace, or something equally dramatic,' said The Woman mischievously.

'Certainly not,' said Holmes, 'the weather's far too nice not to enjoy it to the fullest.' He was glad to hear her laugh, such a contrast from the anxiety of the previous day.

Upon returning to the Keystone Hotel, the two were met with a note from Mina Edison, asking them to dinner once again and explaining that the McGregors would be guests as well. Irene shook her head. 'I can't

191

believe the poor woman even wants us after all this. I'd have thought we were pariahs by now.'

Holmes smiled. 'No reason not to make our thanks in person, especially to Ambrose McGregor, who, it seems to me, has been particularly unfortunate throughout the case.'

'Yes,' said The Woman, 'though I admit I'm not looking forward to seeing everyone I've deceived, good reason or not.'

'Not a compunction that seems to affect you in connection with deceiving me, however,' said the detective drily. Irene gave him a quick look and burst out laughing again, not stopping until they parted at the door to her room.

Holmes dressed elegantly, in the clothing he would have worn for an evening out in London. He was relieved to be himself again, not that he minded playing a part. The end of a case was always pleasant, before the monotony seized him, and he planned to enjoy himself. Irene, too, seemed pleased as she emerged to join him, dressed in a turquoise gown that set off her brown hair and made her look far more like Irene Adler than Lavinia James. He proffered his arm, and the companions went down to catch their cab.

Seminole Lodge was beautiful in the moonlight as they arrived, the grounds lit by paper lanterns that Mina Edison had purchased for the occasion. Holmes led Irene to the door of the white mansion, and she seemed nervous, even more so than she had when she was in the guise of Lavinia James. He lightly squeezed the small hand that held his arm. 'Steady,' he whispered. She was capable of more timidity than he'd expected.

'Good evening, Mr Holmes and Miss Adler,' said Mina Edison without hesitation. She was smiling and radiant.

'Good evening,' said Holmes, smiling down at her kindly.

Irene blushed and nodded as the other woman motioned her inside. 'Marion's wild to see you.' Holmes watched The Woman walk away with the hostess, her confidence obviously rising.

As he entered the piano room, Holmes saw that the dinner party was the same as that of the previous occasion, except that the Montanan cattle rancher had been replaced by the German officer with whom he had seen Marion Edison. The inventor was speaking to the lieutenant, and timid Burroughs was engaged in conversation with Tootie McGregor, whose spirits appeared to be completely restored. As usual, her husband hung back slightly, listening.

Holmes approached Burroughs and held out his hand. 'I must thank you, Sir, for your assistance.'

'I'm grateful I could help,' said the young man. 'The deputies were away from town until morning, so Mr Edison and I figured we could do our part, Mr Holmes.' He stumbled slightly over the name.

Holmes smiled warmly and looked around the group. 'My name is Sherlock Holmes, and my companion is Miss Irene Adler.' He didn't elaborate further, but since he seemed to expect everyone to accept the names, everyone did, out of respect for the detective and his companion. He watched Irene in the corner of the room, engaged in conversation with Marion, and she seemed herself once again.

Dinner was a subdued meal, and no one seemed inclined to mention the case, except for Edison, who asked Irene, seated next to him, whether or not the criminals were in custody. Holmes had noticed that Marion seemed especially nervous and looked often at the German, whose name was Karl Oeser. Finally, she spoke. 'Mr Oeser and I have an announcement.' When all eyes turned toward her, she blushed bright red and took Oeser's hand. 'Mr Oeser-Karl—has asked me to marry him, and I've accepted.'

Holmes looked quickly at Edison and Mina, but neither seemed surprised by the news and both appeared genuinely pleased. Irene beamed across the table. 'I'll sing for you after dinner,' she said to Marion, who couldn't stop smiling. The Woman's equilibrium had returned.

The good feelings remained through dessert, which was a new French recipe called

Crepes Suzette that Mina had ordered to accompany her stepdaughter's announcement. After many compliments, the party finally made its way to the living room, and Irene sat down at the piano. Holmes wondered what sort of song she would choose, if she would again sing the bittersweet anthem that had captivated her audience before. But her fingers began a different tune:

At Clapham Town end lived an Old Yorkshire
  tyke
Who i dealing i horseflesh had ne'er met his
  like.
'Twas his pride that i aw the hard bargains
  he'd hit
He'd bit a good mony but but nivver been bit.
Chorus: Wi'' me dum a dum dary,
Dum a dum dary,
Dum a dum dary,
Dum a dum day.

By the beginning of the second verse, everyone in the room was laughing, and Marion had grabbed Oeser's hand and started to dance. Holmes watched them all is if he were seeing one of Edison's moving pictures, but his eyes were drawn back to The Woman in her element, singing as if nothing else in the world existed. She looked up and smiled at him, and her eyes were warm.

The evening continued with other songs

and impromptu dances, and the members of the party tried to laugh away the darkness as the detective looked on, finally forced to participate by the persistent Tootie, who seized him in her arms and forced him to dance a waltz with her. Marion, alive with joy, played the piano and laughed with the abandon of the young and engaged. Weariness eventually forced the guests to consider leaving, and Irene came to Holmes's side. In spite of the fact that they were no longer portraying a married couple, the proximity seemed normal to both of them, and he gave her his arm once more.

'Thank you for everything!' said Marion, taking Irene's hand. 'I'll miss you.' Her voice was sweet, but she had eyes only for her fiancé, who was quiet and polite and appeared to dote on the girl. He led her away to her father, and the McGregors took her place.

Holmes felt Irene's hand on his arm tense, and he saw that her nervousness had returned when she was confronted with the large woman and the quiet man. He cleared his throat, 'Please accept my apologies for everything that has occurred over these past few days, Mr and Mrs McGregor.' Tootie smiled instantly and gave Holmes a loud kiss on the cheek, which took him aback considerably.

'Don't worry, dear,' she said, 'we're ever so grateful for all you've done. We'd love to read it in a story some time, if Dr Watson has a notion to write it up, of course.' Holmes could feel Irene laughing noiselessly at this, but she gathered herself quickly and turned to Ambrose.

'Mr McGregor,' she said quickly, 'I'm sorry— for everything.' Holmes nodded, adding his own quiet assent. Ambrose smiled one of his rare smiles, an expression that completely changed his face from serious and dour to kind and welcoming in an instant, allowing the detective to finally see what had attracted the gregarious, generous woman to him.

'Miss Adler,' Ambrose said, 'you are an extraordinary woman, and I can only say that Mr Holmes is very fortunate to have your assistance.' The Woman blushed crimson at this, to Holmes's great amusement.

The final goodbye was to the Edisons, who offered their home and company if either Holmes or Irene should ever be in town again. Holmes regretted the necessity of leaving the inventor. He'd have liked to spend a year or more observing the man's work, but it was not to be.

Just before the party broke, Holmes commanded everyone's attention. 'I have a favour to ask of each of you,' he said, making and holding eye contact with every person in the room. 'You now know what kind of people wish me harm. In order to protect me, yourselves, and others from such people, I ask one thing. Do not mention my name or tell anyone that I am alive. You are all bearers of a secret that must not be told.' Wide-eyed stares greeted his request, and one-by-one, each of them nodded in agreement, even Oeser, who seemed to be in awe of the tall Englishman. Holmes didn't suppose they would all keep the promise, but he hoped they would at least manage to do so until he was so far away that even the remaining members of Moriarty's gang could not find him.

Out in the night, the detective could tell by the ease in Irene's movements and breathing that she was relieved. Once they were ensconced in a cab and on the way back to the Keystone, she spoke. 'Now I feel like it's really over, Holmes.'

'As do I,' he replied. 'I don't like facing the consequences of necessary deception any more than you do.' She nodded.

'I understand, Holmes. I don't know how you always manage it.'

'One builds up walls of objectivity.'

'I don't think I could,' she said, a slightly brittle note in her voice. The night had been difficult for her.

'Your singing was marvellous.'

'Thank you, Holmes.'

'You're welcome.' He smiled, and she returned his with one of her own.

'I took the liberty of consulting a train schedule,' he said after a while. 'I'll speak to

Morris in the morning, and we should be free to leave by ten o'clock, if you wish it.'

'I do,' Irene answered.

Chapter 19: Irene

That night, I tried to sleep, but I couldn't stop thinking about the future. Holmes had promised that Mycroft would make sure I was taken care of until my assets were sorted, so I didn't worry about money, but I felt adrift. Singing had been one purpose and the case another, but now I no longer had a desire to sing or a case to concern me. I supposed I would go to London, where I had been before all my trouble started. I had no family to return to in America, and the great British metropolis seemed like my most sensible option, a place I had lived and with which I was intimately familiar. I didn't look forward to the press of people and the call of society, but I had nowhere else to go, and I knew that Holmes must move on as well. Somehow, as unexpected as it was to realise, I knew that I would miss him.

The next morning was appropriately gloomy, with a light rain and grey clouds overhead as we made for the train station. Holmes had visited the policeman while I dressed, and he assured me that Morris had understood Mycroft's telegram and agreed that not only Holmes, but I as well, should be kept out of further record or investigation. I was vastly thankful to Mycroft, though I never expected to meet him and express the sentiment. Holmes assured me that, like his own, his brother's work was its own reward.

As the train carried us away from Fort Myers, I felt as if I had spent far longer there than the days actually indicated. The journey to New York was to take us through the night and the following day, and after that, Holmes and I would part. It seemed strange to leave one another as suddenly as we had come back into each other's lives.

I sat back in my seat and studied my companion. His long fingers flipped the pages of his newspaper with rapid dexterity, and his eyes flitted from column to column like a fly hopping from one thing to another, taking in all the things he deemed important and leaving the rest. His body was relaxed, and he looked slightly less gaunt than he had at the height of the case, though he would never be anything other than spare.

After a long while, Holmes looked up and met my eyes. 'I have an offer to make to you, Irene,' he said slowly. 'You told me that you desired nothing more than a quiet life.'

'That's true,' I answered.

'I own a cottage on the Sussex Downs,' he continued. 'It's small—nothing grand or luxurious, but situated in a picturesque part of the country. No one lives there at present, but a lady named Mrs Turner takes care of it for me. I had intended to keep it for my eventual retirement.

'I offer this home to you, for your use.' He looked down, as if slightly embarrassed. 'I offer it as a friend.

'As you know, I'm supposed to be dead, and I do not know if I will ever return to England to live. Watson and Mycroft are the only others who know of the property's existence. Without me, Watson has no reason to ever think of the place again, and Mycroft will never trouble you. You'd have no companions unless you sought them for yourself. The place would be yours entirely, for as long as you cared to remain there.'

'I'll think about it,' I replied quietly.

I thought about it. My mind turned to nothing else as we barreled toward separation. Holmes's offer had nothing to do with money. We were both wealthy, the man who couldn't return home and the woman with no home to return to. I longed for quiet, for contemplation, for a place where my weary mind could rest. Sussex was exactly what I desired, a place where I could be inconspicuous and do as I wished, where the world would not trouble me, nor I it. I accepted Holmes's offer an hour before we reached New York.

'Where will you go?' I asked my companion.

'Tibet,' he answered. I saw a gleam in his eye, and I knew that he looked forward to his journey. Because of his kindness, I also looked forward to mine. I felt at peace as we pulled into the station.

Holmes and I parted outside the Central New York Railway. 'I trust you have enough money to take you to Sussex. Mycroft will send more within the month,' he said, concern on his face. I nodded.

'I do.'

'Be careful. We don't know where Moran may have eyes and ears.'

'And you, Holmes.' The tall detective leaned forward and touched my face for a moment, tracing my cheekbone with his finger, and then he was gone. He disappeared in a crowd of people down the street, blending in the way he was always so capable of doing. I watched the spot where he'd been a moment before, as if he might somehow magically reappear. Then, I squared my shoulders, turned around, and went to book a passage to England.

*　　*　　*

On the Sussex Downs, time had an odd way of passing. The days seemed long and luxurious, unburdened by the speed of the world and the concerns of others in it, but the years, in contrast, passed quickly, as if they'd come and gone without my notice. I learned to garden and cook and clean, all things Mrs Turner was more than willing to do for me, but that I desired to do for myself after a lifetime of being waited on by others. I began to feel self-sufficient, like a stronger version of the weary Irene Adler who had dragged herself into the cottage after a grueling ocean passage.

I liked living alone more than I ever would have before James Barnett's gun had made me confront my own fears. I liked waking up to the sound of my own thoughts and then choosing who would share them, if anyone. I became friends with women in the village who simply knew me as the widow Irene who lived on the hill. They did not intrude on my life any more than I desired, since their families clamored for their work and attention, and I even became friendly with their husbands and children. I was somewhat of a mystery, I knew, but I appreciated the locals' willingness to let me have my secrets. I believe they enjoyed having such an eccentric resident among them.

After a year, I bought a piano. At first, I only sang for myself, but after one of the village farm wives walked up the hill and heard me practicing, I became something of a desired commodity. I played for funerals and sang at weddings, and I enjoyed being a part of the life of the community as much as I had ever liked singing under theatrical lights.

My other passion was my bees. I discovered them as a result of my habit of subscribing to all sorts of magazines and journals. I was happy to lead an uneventful village life, but I still enjoyed reading about the exploits of others and learning what I could about many things, so I collected many periodicals, one of which was published by naturalists. One day, I came across an article about beekeeping, a perfectly normal sort of animal husbandry analysis of which the publication was inordinately fond, but I was intrigued in a way I had not been before. I pored over the drawings of hives and the advice about how to make the environment harmonious enough for good honey to be produced. The information about bee existence fascinated me—their logical, methodical lives that all contributed to the good of their society. The perfect collectivists, bees.

Soon, I ordered one book about beekeeping and then another. I thought the passion was to be a purely academic one, a quest to learn all I could about the bee kingdom and amuse myself by applying what I knew in my imagination, but the itch became too strong. I determined that I must have bees.

I spent months methodically acquiring all the necessary equipment, crowing with delight over the bee paradise I intended to create. Finally, the creatures themselves arrived, buzzing with life, and I became a beekeeper.

I didn't love the pastime at first, and I made many mistakes, some of which angered the bees and resulted in painful stings. But I kept at it. After several months, my hives were in good order, and I was devoted to beekeeping in earnest.

*   *   *

One windy morning in April, I went to my hives to check on the bees and see how they were getting on. I'd been in Fulworth nearly three years then, though I rarely thought about the passage of time. I was due to sing for a wedding the following Saturday, and I hummed a love song to myself, hoping the weather would be nice for the couple.

Unbidden, my mind turned to the disturbing tale I'd read in the newspaper that morning. Reportedly, a London man named Ronald Adair had been shot in a seemingly impossible way—by soft-nosed revolver bullet in a locked room that had no signs of being breached. The story was strange enough to reach even the country papers, and I tried to reason it out for myself, though Scotland Yard was reportedly baffled by the scene.

I thought of Holmes then, of course. I wondered what he'd have said about the case, whether it was one he'd have solved simply from reading the account, or if he'd have wanted to inspect the scene. Those thoughts brought others forward, and a pang inside me told me that I still missed my friend. Very few days went by that I failed to think of him, because my gratefulness for the life he'd offered me was often in my mind. I wondered if he was still in Tibet, or if he was even still alive. The world, at least the small part I inhabited and the larger part I read about, seemed to bear no imprint of the detective's life whatsoever.

Later that day, I went into the village to purchase dry goods at the shop on Lamb Street, and I was met by a disturbance. Lionel Warren, who operated the village's seldom-used telegraph, was standing on the street surrounded by Mr Sykes, who owned the shop, and Mrs Carlyle and Miss Rose of Wilmont Farm, all of them speaking over each other in excited voices.

'There's a telegram for you!' said Miss Rose excitedly as I approached. Lionel nodded, his eyes bulging. 'First telegram I've had in weeks!'

I was surprised that I'd received a telegram at all, but its contents shocked me far more:

Coming to visit 12th on 9:40 if convenient STOP and *Watson* STOP *Please advise* STOP *SH*

I gave my affirmative reply to Lionel in a shaky voice that he interpreted to be the result of my amazement at the immense honour of receiving a telegram, and then walked home, my heart beating rapidly. Holmes, alive in England! And then the doubts began. What if someone was impersonating Holmes to get to me? I began sleeping with my pistol near my pillow and listening for any odd noises in the night. Florida had been far away for some time, both in place and memory, but the case returned to my mind with absolute clarity. I dreamed about the face of James Barnett, long in jail, and the dead young man who'd threatened to put a bullet in my head. In my waking hours, I hoped for Holmes.

April 12th was a beautiful day, sunny and pleasant, and I went to the train station early in the morning to wait for my visitors. I took a seat on a bench, keeping my hand on the gun inside my bag. I hadn't carried it even once since my arrival in Sussex, but I didn't want to take a chance that one of Holmes's enemies would be getting off the train.

I had hardly let myself think about what I would say to the detective or how I would feel when I saw him. The strength of my anticipation had surprised me, and I was glad, too, to think that Dr Watson was no longer grieving as the result of a deception. But I had no idea how I would respond when the spare form stepped off the train. I had supposed for so long that he would never come that my mind had trouble accepting the notion that he would soon appear.

I was still lost in thought when the train arrived. Startled by the noise, I came out to watch the passengers disembark, but only two emerged: a short man in a bowler hat and a tall man with piercing eyes.

Chapter 20: Holmes

Irene was the only person on the platform. Holmes watched her as the train pulled into the station, noting with approval that her hand was inside her handbag, no doubt clutching her firearm in case she should need it. She looked well, better than she had been in Florida, with colour in her cheeks and bright, clear eyes. Fulworth had agreed with her, as he'd known it would.

Watson got off the train first, complimenting the country air, and Holmes followed. Three long years he'd been away from England, and even now he'd only been in London for a few weeks. He'd missed the English countryside. He'd also missed the company of The Woman, which he hadn't expected. She stood calmly, waiting and watching. He wondered if she was pleased to see him.

'Good afternoon, Miss Adler,' said Watson in his gallant way, stopping in front of Irene.

'Dr Watson, I'm glad to see you.' Her smile

showed relief.

'Not at all,' said the small man, smiling broadly, 'it's Holmes we're all pleased to see.' He meant it, Holmes knew. John Watson hadn't given more than a moment's thought to his years of thinking his best friend was dead. He'd simply accepted things as they were and his friend back into his life.

'Indeed we are,' said The Woman, smiling first at the doctor and then up at the detective.

'I'm glad to see you well,' he said.

'Likewise,' she answered. It felt natural to be with her again, as if mere days had passed since the Floridian case.

*   *   *

That night, Mrs Turner insisted on cooking the two men their favourite foods, almost as excited to see the younger Holmes as Irene seemed to be. That was the thing that gave the detective the most satisfaction. For all The Woman's calm coolness, he could tell that she was genuinely delighted to see him, and he was glad.

Watson went to bed early in the evening, tired from the journey and eager to read his beloved medical journals, but Holmes and Irene stayed up late into the night, talking and drinking tea. They spoke about Florida, and then he told her in detail about the case of Ronald Adair and how it had intertwined with the apprehension of Sebastian Moran. He could see the worry leave her as he finished his tale, as if some part of her that had remained tense ever since the Floridian case had now relaxed.

'Thank you for telling me, Holmes,' she said quietly. 'Now, will you tell me about your time away?'

The question was so artless that it took Holmes by surprise. He hadn't intended to tell Irene about the dark nights and hungry days or the near-misses and tense moments, but he found himself doing so, more fully than he had told anyone else. His words painted the simple life of the Dalai Lama, the fjords of Norway, and the worshippers of Mecca. She even wrinkled her nose as he described the tar pits of France.

'I nearly returned to Tibet at the last,' he said, as he neared the end of his tale. 'It is curious how many similarities exist between the life of the logician and the life of the mystic.'

'But you came back to England.'

'Yes, I came back.'

'Why?'

'It was The Game, Irene. I am hardly suited to a life of contemplation.' She laughed then, and he enjoyed hearing it as much as he had three years before.

'And what of you?' he asked after a moment.

She smiled mischievously. 'I am a beekeeper.'

He stared at her a moment, wondering if she was joking, but her eyes were serious.

'Logical creatures, bees,' he said. *Like we two*, he thought to himself, but he didn't say it aloud.

The next morning, she showed him her hives. He watched as she carefully, almost reverently, opened each door and pointed to queen and subjects, explaining the functions of each part of the society. It was odd, Holmes thought, how much it suited her. She was at home in this activity that seemed simple on the surface but was vastly intricate and complex just below it. Her perceptive mind took pleasure in the tiny details that made her hives the pinnacle of perfection, and she cared not one whit if any other human being ever knew or cared. The detective admired her precision, but he knew that he could not have borne such serenity. He needed friction to keep his engine running, but she was like a tree that simply needed the earth and the air.

She was different here, freer. Her world was smaller, but she was less constrained within it, less wary and afraid. He no longer heard the brittle bitterness that her voice had contained before. She was once again the Irene Adler who had fooled the greatest detective in the world. No, he thought, she was more. She was older and more complete, and happiness sat well on her.

The three friends walked to the station five days later, amid Dr Watson's effusive compliments to Miss Adler's home, which she received with a smile. She truly liked the little doctor, and that fact gratified Holmes. Watson bid The Woman fond farewell at the train, but Holmes was silent, and his eyes were upon her as the locomotive pulled away.

Once again, she was alone on the platform. She was dressed in a brown skirt and blue shirtwaist, a plain outfit, but her face was anything but plain. The eyes that watched him depart were deep and quiet, and the mouth was ironic, as if The Woman would be ready to make a joke at any moment. But her hair— her chestnut hair was bundled loosely on her head, far wilder than she'd ever worn it in her life before the cottage. The day was windy, and pieces of it had escaped and framed her face. She lifted a hand and waved goodbye to the detective, and he waved in return.

Holmes didn't know when, but he knew he would come again.

*   *   *

It was two years before the detective again made his way up the hill to the little house. This time he was alone, since Watson had chosen to attend a medical conference in Zurich. As before, he found The Woman in good health and spirits, and pleased, as ever, by her bees. She had purchased more hives, and now the honey they produced had begun to bring her a small income, which amused her greatly.

For three days, they roamed the countryside together, and Holmes told Irene about plants both poisonous and curative. She seemed far from alarmed when he explained the connections of various herbs to cases he'd solved, and the accounts of even the most grisly of murders appeared to interest rather than sicken her. He acted out for her the circumstances one of his more mysterious cases in which a body had been found with no tracks leading to its resting place, using the Sussex grass as his stage, and she clapped delightedly and solved the case herself before he'd told her the solution.

The third night, he found himself discussing his current case, a slow, delicate affair involving a foreign head of state, which had required him to be absent from London for a short time. Irene listened intently before offering her own thoughts, to which Holmes listened objectively. That night he did not sleep, but he considered what The Woman had said and realised that it might help him reach a solution. When he left for London two days later, he asked if he might write to her in future and ask for her opinion of perplexing cases.

So began a correspondence that was sometimes frequent and copious and other times filled with long silences. If Irene helped Holmes and Dr Watson with several cases after that, no one ever knew, and if her opinion occasionally kept them from erring, Watson promised to keep her secret and never write a word of it in his stories.

The detective visited the white cottage twice the next year, both times after the end of a case when dreaded boredom gnawed at his mind. Each time, he found the woman unchanged, except, if possible, that her company was even more restful and her wit more engaging. Each time, too, she succeeded in drawing him out and keeping his mind occupied until a new problem presented itself.

After that, he came to Sussex whenever he was between cases, sometimes with Watson and other times alone. No doubt the villagers wondered about the relationship between the tall man and the lady beekeeper, but they kept their thoughts to themselves because they liked her, and after a long time, they began to like the man as well, in spite of his strange ways.

*   *   *

Holmes had noticed Irene's piano during his first visit, and he'd been glad to see that she had not abandoned her music. In subsequent visits, he often brought his violin to Fulworth and spent many evenings playing whatever she or Watson requested. At those times, he wished The Woman would follow suit, but he did not press her, and she did not offer.

Christmas Eve of 1902 was different. Holmes came to the cottage alone, as Watson had chosen to spend the holiday with his family. The doctor had been unwell, and the detective believed he might soon retire from medical practice. He, too, no longer felt young, but when he saw The Woman waiting for him on the platform, those thoughts vanished.

How was it possible, he wondered, that she had stayed the same? The world had changed—Mycroft had told him that international war would not be long in coming, and even London, his friend of so many years, was beginning to fill with motorcars instead of hansom cabs. But Irene Adler looked the same as the girl who had so cheerfully beaten him more than a decade before.

'Good morning, Holmes,' she said, taking his arm. He could tell that she was cold in the December chill, so he took off his wool scarf and wrapped it around her neck. She smiled up at him, and they continued up the hill in companionable silence.

They spent the day visiting the bees and talking about cases they had solved, until evening came and Holmes opened the bottle of champagne he had brought to mark the holiday. 'To your health, Miss Adler,' he said, raising his glass to her.

'And to yours, Holmes.' Her spirits were unusually high, and the detective tried for several moments to deduce the cause, but he could not.

Finally, when she had drunk her fill of the golden liquid, Irene went to the piano on the far side of the room and sat down at it, smiling at Holmes. 'I would like to sing tonight,' she said quietly, her eyes shining.

She lifted the lid of the instrument, and he could see in her face that the act was significant beyond the present. When she began to play, he understood why. The song was becoming old-fashioned then, reminiscent of a vanishing time, but it was the song between The Woman and the detective.

Oh, promise me that someday you and I
Will take our love together to some sky
Where we can be alone and faith renew,
And find the hollows where those flowers grew

He looked into her eyes, and for the first time, she was singing to him.§

Epilogue

Baker Street
December 10, 1903

Dear Irene,

These separations between visits grow irksome, and as Watson declares his intention of soon limiting his practice to near-retirement, I shall come down on the 20th by the 8:00, with no intention of ever returning to Baker Street. I think—I hope, at least, that this will be as congenial a prospect to you as it is to me and, of course, to your bees.

Yours,
S.H.

Fulworth
December 15th, 1903

My Dear Holmes,
The bees find your message quite congenial, as do I. I will meet your train, and you will find me prepared to become Mrs Holmes.

Yours,
Irene

Afterword

Several of the individuals mentioned in this story walked the streets of Fort Myers, Florida, at the turn of the 20th century, though they might be surprised to return and find themselves part of a case involving the great detective Sherlock Holmes. Thomas Edison and his second wife Mina spent many happy winters at Seminole Lodge. Marion Edison married Lieutenant Karl Oeser and lived with him in Germany until 1921. John Murphy built a beautiful home that was later bought by N elson Burroughs and his wife, who became prominent citizens of Fort Myers. Tootie and Ambrose McGregor also made Fort Myers their permanent home, and Tootie was a respected humanitarian and citizen, whose contributions to her city are still enjoyed. Both the Edison and Burroughs homes are historic sites today.